The Cost-Effective
Use of Leeches
And
Other Musings Of A
Medical School Survivor

The Cost-Effective Use of Leeches

And
Other Musings Of A
Medical School Survivor

Jeffrey A. Drayer, M.D.

Galen Press, Ltd.
Tucson, Arizona

Special bulk purchase terms are available, contact our special sales department.
Galen Press, Ltd., P.O. Box 64400, Tucson, AZ 85728-4400
Phone (520) 577-8363 Fax (520) 529-6459 Orders (U.S./Canada) 1-800-442-5369

Library of Congress Cataloging-in-Publication Data
Drayer, Jeffrey A.
    The cost-effective use of leeches and other musings of a medical
  school survivor / Jeffrey A. Drayer.
        p.   cm.
    ISBN 1-883620-13-9 (pbk.)
    1. Medical education--Miscellanea.   2. Medical education--Humor.
  I. Title.
  R737.D72 1998
  610'.71'1--dc21   98-25829

Printed in the United States of America.

10 9 8 7 6 5 4 3 2 1

Dedication

To my Parents (whom I love so much), who encouraged
me to do everything I wanted;

To Brian, whose opinion matters;

and

to all the people at Duke University Medical Center
who understood just what it is that I'm saying.

Perhaps, in the end, cynicism is
nothing more than frustrated love.

Table Of Contents

You Wrote A Book?!

The question I'm asked most frequently these days after "Why won't you stop calling me?" is "How did a guy like you write a book?" This is a reasonable question: before medical school, I'd never really shown a propensity for writing or, actually, for communicating in any way. When future generations look back upon my life and try to make some sense of it, they will notice that, for many years, my life was very ordinary. I had a normal family, a few friends brave enough to be seen with me in public, four very nondescript years at college, and a year working as a research assistant in a lab. Then came a journey down to North Carolins, and the start of four years of medical school. And that was when everything changed.

When you watch the movies, which is basically where I made my decision to go to medical school, you always see young, attractive, intelligent people with the common noble goal of healing the sick. They work hard, but it is in the quest of a higher purpose, and suddenly, especially when the movie only lasts ninety minutes, medical school doesn't seem like a bad idea. After all, the guy always gets the girl he loves, passes his classes with highest honors, gains the respect of everyone around him, and sets himself on the road toward a life of service and happiness. And when you think that you too could make enough money to live on while being altruistic, going to med school seems like a darn good idea.

Now, I'm not saying it's necessarily a *bad* idea. It's just that there are things going on in the big world of Medicine that they don't tell you about in the movies or, for that matter, in the medical school brochures. When you apply to med school, you wonder what it's going to be like to deal with sick patients, whether you can learn the enormous amount of information, and whether you can handle the grueling hours all this requires.

What you don't realize—until it's too late to get your money back—is that far above everything else, medical school involves learning to deal with a lot of different people, not all of whom watched the same movies that you did. Many of these people, it seems, are there simply to make you unhappy. There are surgeons who ask you impossible question after impossible question during an operation until you finally contaminate yourself and have to leave. There are residents who keep you after work for hours to discuss the fifty most likely causes for a cough in a patient with culture-proven pneumonia, and nurses who think they know everything about medicine despite never having had any actual training. There are physician assistants with an inferiority complex the size of my liver and whose first sentence to any medical student is always "I could've gone to med school, you know, but I made a lifestyle decision." And there are enormous Hospital Unit Coordinators (HUCs) who sit around all day eating hamburgers and not answering phones, whose very purpose, it seems, is to keep vital medical information from students so that they look stupid on rounds. In medical school, you are engaged in a daily battle, a struggle to prevent these people, intent on making you miserable, from winning. And they're very good at what they do.

When faced with this cast of characters, coupled with the already overwhelming pressure to learn a ton of information that is both complicated and boring, med students find various ways of coping. Some focus solely on being a physician and do whatever it takes to become one. Others try to ignore the nonsense around them and maintain as healthy and as friendly an attitude as possible. Some despair and become anesthesiologists. But me? I became editor of the newspaper and I wrote about it.

Many people believe that this was a good form of therapy for me, a way to work through the difficult times and moments of doubt. Others feel it was a way for me to ask the questions that I thought were important in an open forum to provoke discussion among the medical community. Actually, though, I did it because I like to hear myself talk. *Shifting Dullness*, the med school newspaper, gave me the opportunity to say whatever I felt like and it forced people to listen.

Throughout med school I learned many lessons. Not lessons such as which antiarrhythmic to prescribe for atrial fibrillation or how to read a chest x-ray— my patients can certainly testify to that. What I did learn was, I believe, far more valuable. I learned how to take lots of free drug samples and get away with it. I learned how to get grad students to do my research project for me and still get to be first author on the resulting paper. And I learned that, no matter how convincing a movie's special effects may be, in real life, med school is not exactly the same as it is portrayed in the movies.

These are the kinds of lessons I wrote about, each as hard for me to believe as the renal system. But, in the end, the most important lesson I learned came from writing the essays themselves. I learned that if you open up your heart and write everything that's within it as honestly as you possibly can, the results will be insulting to some, despicable to others, and outright crazy to most. So much so, in fact, that people will begin to take it for granted and, after a while, they won't even bother to get mad. And that, I believe, is when you've finally won.

No, medical school, as it turned out, was not like the movies at all. But that isn't necessarily bad. I got the chance to experience some strange people and even stranger situations. Maybe I'm even a better person for it. Perhaps, in fact, I have written my own movie. So, as you read through this book, imagine everything very vividly and visualize my character being played by Brad Pitt. If it looks good, let the people down in Hollywood know. I could be looking for a new job pretty soon anyway.

A Curriculum Fit For A King

The King University School of Medicine curriculum differs from those of other medical schools in one very distinct way—King Med doesn't actually teach their students very much about medicine.

This is, of course, an oversimplification. You see, King Med believes that future doctors should have a thorough understanding of the process and function of biomedical research, which is very admirable. To gain the kind of experience necessary to appreciate this facet of medicine, each student must spend a year as the principal investigator in a research project of his or her choice. Again, very admirable. However, something has to be sacrificed to free up an entire year for research. That thing ends up being basic science, the foundation of medicine.

The traditional medical school curriculum involves two years of basic science in which, I'm told, students are taught such subjects as gross anatomy, physiology, pathology, pharmacology, and microbiology, each lasting anywhere from four months to a year. After this, students generally get a few weeks to study for Step 1 of the USMLE (or "Medical Boards"), which covers the basic science they supposedly just learned. Then, in the third year, the beleaguered students are finally let loose onto the hospital wards for their clerkships in surgery, obstetrics and gynecology, pediatrics, internal medicine, and so forth. During the fourth year, students take elective rotations in subjects they are interested in or, at least, in subjects they pretend to be interested in because they have easy hours and no nights on call. The winter of this year is spent applying and interviewing for residencies. Finally, one day in the middle of May, students take the Hippocratic Oath and officially become doctors.

King Med, with its admirable interest in providing research experience, sets aside the third year for students to spend in the lab. This means that the normal third-year clerkships are done in the second year and the two years normally spent on basic science are squeezed into one very long, very tiring year.

For example, take gross anatomy. The human body has a lot of parts, including nerves, arteries, muscles, bones, and something called the "spleen." Most med schools recognize this and provide five or six months of daily lectures and hours in the dissection lab, allowing their med students to become thoroughly familiar with the human body upon which they will practice the healing arts for their entire careers. King Med gives you seven weeks, every other day. Immunology, the intricate study of how the body attempts to fight off disease, is usually given between two and five months. King Med allows four weeks. Embryology, which covers how the systems of the body develop in synchrony to form a whole, living human being, is often taught for a month or two. King Med students are encouraged to learn about it in their spare time.

Not surprisingly, the King Med system creates some problems. Most notably, students don't know very much about medicine when they reach the wards. Somehow, though, everyone muddles through, often despite the disgust of attendings who trained at more traditional medical schools. However, it all comes back to haunt King Med students at the end of their third year, the research year, when they are forced to take Step 1 of the USMLE (inappropriately labeled "U-SMILE").

As a result of the intensive first year, there's no time to take Step 1, which covers all the basic sciences, including embryology, before beginning the second-year clerkships. After a year on the wards, during which most students begin to forget their basic science after realizing it has absolutely nothing to do with being a doctor, the research year begins. Throughout this year, the students forget the rest of their basic science as well as the clinical medicine they just learned. Instead, for nine months or so, the average King Med student knows only the intricate details of whatever insignificant protein he's desperately trying to sequence. Then, the end of the third year arrives and suddenly it's time to take Step 1. Understandably, there's a bit of a panic, since this twelve-hour, zillion-question test covers all the information that the students barely knew and have long since forgotten.

But after that, the students are home free. Well, almost. Because even though they need only take a bunch of easy elective rotations with light call schedules to graduate, they must apply to residencies throughout the fall and winter so that they have a job when the big day comes.

This application process, which is the same for every U.S. medical student, requires each student to first choose the specialty he wants to eventually practice and to then apply to the programs he wants to attend. After two months traveling around the country on interviews, during which he does a lot of lying, the student ranks the programs in order of preference, sends in his list, and then holds his breath in anticipation of Match Day.

Match Day is the day when every fourth-year med student crowds into an auditorium and, exactly at noon, receives an envelope. That envelope contains the information that determines the direction of the rest of the student's life: where and in what specialty he will be doing his internship and residency.

After that, it's only two more months until graduation and "Doctordom." After a relaxing month of vacation, saying good-byes, and relocating to a new city, the new doctor begins a one-year internship, followed (hopefully) by several years of residency in the chosen specialty. Finally, our once-humble medical student will become an "Attending" physician, the top of the heap, where he can spend his days answering to insurance companies and being the "sole responsible party" in malpractice suits.

Well, that's the overview of the King Med curriculum, and beyond. Who knows? If I'd gotten this type of information when I was a college senior, I might have a well-paying job on Wall Street today.

A Personalized Lexicon

Autovalet: The enormous, ominous-looking scrub-dispensing machines recently placed in the surgery locker rooms to prevent scrub theft. Luckily, I stole seventeen pairs before their installation so that I wouldn't have to deal with them and the nightmares they would eventually cause those who did.

Bovey: The name of the pen-shaped cautery used by surgeons to seal (by melting closed) small bleeding vessels. This process is called "buzzing," prompting one nervous second-year med student, when ordered to buzz by an attending surgeon, to timidly say "bzzzz."

CABG: Pronounced like the disgusting vegetable, but not nearly as healthy. Stands for Coronary Artery Bypass Graft, the indications for which, at King, are having experienced chest pain within the last five years and possessing a heart.

Chimeric mouse: An animal genetically altered and used for research studies. Apparently, however, this is only 5/14ths of the correct explanation, at least according to the professor who graded my genetics test.

ERAS: Pronounced "E-rass." The new Electronic Residency Application Service, in which applicants (only in certain specialties) input their information onto a computer disk and then select which programs to send it to. Somehow, such a simple-sounding system, despite costing the med student about half a year's rent, has worked very, very poorly.

Harrison's: The Bible of internal medicine, despite the fact that Dr. Harrison has been dead since before the discovery of antibiotics. Students would carry this around with them every waking minute if it didn't weigh eighty-three pounds.

HEENT: The Head, Eyes, Ears, Nose and Throat section of a physical exam. Almost always noted as "normal," unless the person is actually missing an ear—or a throat.

Hematoxylin: Along with eosin, the most common stain used on pathology slides—turns everything within a five-mile radius a pretty shade of red.

H&P: History and Physical. Often performed by the med student on a new patient shortly after it was performed by both the resident and the intern. Usually takes one to two hours per patient, or four to five for a VA Hospital patient.

HUC: Hospital Unit Coordinator. Not to generalize, but these are usually grossly overweight, uneducated women whose "job" is to run the daily business of each ward, including answering phones, paging doctors, taking orders off the charts, and sending blood work to the lab. Somehow, this involves spending a lot of time gossiping and eating doughnuts.

Jaundiced: The yellow color your newborn infant has if his liver isn't working well. If this pigment gets into his developing brain (kernicterus), he's in real trouble. It's why we have a legal minimum drinking age.

Match Day: The dreaded Third Wednesday of March, on which, at High Noon, every fourth-year med student lines up and receives an envelope which reveals the location of their internship and residency.

MCAT: Medical College Admission Test. Evil standardized exam that tests a college student's ability to take standardized tests. This is a big factor in getting into med school. Miraculously, it didn't stop me.

MICU: Medical Intensive Care Unit. If you're a patient here, you're in real trouble, and not just because all your doctors are pulmonologists on call every other night.

MRSA: Methicillin-Resistant *Staphlococcus Aureus.* If your bug is resistant to methicillin (an antibiotic), it may be time to try out the vancomycin (the "ultimate" antibiotic).

MS-I through IV: MS-I stands for a first-year med student; MS-IV stands for fourth-year students. MS, incidentally, stands for "medical student," not "mindless slave," as some interns seem to think.

Open-ended question: A technique for talking to patients that is taught in Clinical Arts. It involves asking questions in such a way that the patient must give more information than simply "yes" or "no." Usually results in forty-minute-long answers, of which the first thirty-nine minutes usually have nothing to do with the question. Medical students learn not to ask these questions within minutes after meeting their first actual patient.

PALS: The Peri-Arteriolar-Lymphatic System, which med students are told can be seen in microscopic sections of the spleen. Most students cannot see them.

PERLA: Pupils equal, react to light and accommodation. One of the things written in the HEENT (see above) portion of the physical exam notes. More than anything, it's a code to the resident signifying that the med student didn't examine the patient's eyes at all.

PIMPing: Put In My Place. When someone of higher rank asks medical questions to someone of a lower rank. The process usually ends only when the person of lower rank finally gets something wrong, making the person of higher rank feel like a big shot. In psychiatric terms, this ritual is a "defense mechanism" used by people with low self-confidence.

Reed-Sternberg cell: Alleged histopathologic sign of Hodgkin's lymphoma. If someone tells you they see the "characteristic owl eyes," you know they're lying. It's sort of like hearing a Grade I (soft, unhearable sound) heart murmur.

Sib: At King Med, every incoming MS-I gets picked by an MS-II, usually based upon such strict criteria as being of the opposite sex, and therefore becomes this MS-II's "little sib." The MS-II's duties include helping the new student get oriented, answering any questions, lending textbooks, and passing on the test file, which contains all the tests from the past several years. The MS-I's responsibilities include ignoring the big sib's advice and laughing at their old tests.

SOAP: Subjective, Objective, Assessment, and Plan. This format is used for all physician and student notes written in the medical chart. No one ever reads anything in the chart but the Plan. Med students are expected to write a page per patient each day, even though they never quite know what the Plan is.

Sonometer: Actually, the way physicians pronounce the word "centimeter." No one is sure why they do this. Centimeter is very easy to pronounce and hard to confuse with any other word. This is one of the great mysteries of modern medicine.

Tunica vaginalis: The little piece of abdominal tissue dragged down into the testicles by the descending testes. A totally useless piece of anatomy. Of course, I've felt the same way sometimes about my testes.

UTI: Urinary Tract Infection. 'Nuf said.

Vancomycin: The biggest, toughest antibiotic you can prescribe. By the time a patient needs this, they are often what is clinically known as "screwed."

Xanthines: The stuff in coffee that keeps you awake. Caffeine is one. I think. I'll check later.

BOOK ONE

How Did A Guy Like You Write A Book?

The Cost-Effective Use of Leeches and Other Musings of a Medical School Survivor

In The Beginning

I parked my car in the unfamiliar garage and got out. Orienting myself toward the top two floors of the hospital, which rose above the nearby hotels and parking decks, I began my first long walk to the medical school. And as I walked, I began to think about how it was, in many ways, symbolic of the long journey I'd made to arrive at this day. All those years in junior high, high school, and college spent studying hard and keeping my grades up, while making the difficult transition from childhood to becoming an adult. During that time, I constantly looked within myself, wondering just what place I would occupy in the world, trying to discover my niche. Now, as I entered through the sliding glass door and turned down the hallway to the auditorium, I realized that I had, indeed, only passed through one set of what would be countless doors before I was through. Everything I had done led up to this, yet it was only the start of a lifetime of learning. This was the beginning, in fact, of a whole new journey—the journey toward becoming a doctor.

I entered the auditorium and eased into the third seat in the second-to-last row as my thoughts turned to the upcoming lecture, my first in medical school. This would be my first encounter with the life-and-death decisions, the secret knowledge, the enormous responsibility that went with being a healer. What would this first lecture be about? I became increasingly anxious as I realized this was the moment I had waited for, worked for. The professor ascended the steps to the podium. What wise words would he give me? What arcane and powerful knowledge would I have within minutes that I didn't have now? I could only wait, on the edge of my seat.

"Good morning everyone," he began. "My name is Dr. Meniscus and today I'll be talking about a subject very important to me." I gripped the seat cushion and learned forward. "I'd like to talk to you," he continued, "about the receptor for 5-dihydrotestosterone in the prostate, which my research seems to show is somehow linked with benign prostatic hypertrophy." Medical school had begun.

I sat there, listening attentively as he talked on and on about stuff that apparently had something to do with the prostate. I took copious notes, transcribing every valuable word for future reference. If the curriculum committee thought that these were the pearls of wisdom I would need to become a good doctor, then I would learn them. I scribbled furiously, feeling the information pass from my pen to my paper and then, slowly, to my brain. I wrote until my wrist hurt, but fought back the pain with the sheer desire to learn. Until suddenly I had a revelation. It was an epiphany such as I had only heard about in Greek legend. Though I didn't know it at the time, it was possibly the most valuable lesson I would learn in medical school. *I realized that the professor's entire lecture was on the handout!*

I put down my pen and sat, momentarily paralyzed. I couldn't just get up and leave in the middle of the very first lecture of medical school. But then it occurred to me that perhaps the purpose of giving out lecture notes was to allow us to devote our full attention to listening to the professor. With renewed excitement, I sat back, intending to absorb all the wisdom I could.

Within ten minutes I was lost. I didn't know what a prostate was, or where testosterone came from. Why did we need to discuss sodium ion pumps? What was so bad about this "hypertrophy"? My attention waned and, eventually, wandered to the newspaper lying on the floor and the crossword puzzle on page sixteen. "Twenty across: Large leg bone." I had no idea.

The next four hours went by fairly painlessly. I finished the crossword puzzle, read *USA Today*'s sports section (including the color graphs), and ate a doughnut. In between these activities, I observed what medical students are really like.

And so began medical school. The next few days passed similarly, as I collected handouts that dealt with things I couldn't even begin to understand. But what I understood less was what these things had to do with being a doctor. I mean, was it really important that I knew the five sub-units of a transmembrane receptor to help someone recover from a heart attack? Did I need to know the molecular weight of each kind of lipoprotein so I would some day be able to mend a broken wrist? I really wasn't sure. But one thing I did know, it certainly was boring.

So, after years of undergraduate biology and chemistry classes that were designed, presumably, to determine whether I was fit to someday become a doctor, here I was, taking yet more science classes, unsure what I was supposed to be getting out of them. I had all the notes so I wasn't worried about passing the tests. But was I getting any closer to becoming a doctor? It was hard to tell. I looked back down at my crossword puzzle. "Eleven down: Number of chambers in the heart." I still had no idea.

Cynical Arts

Only the first set of midterms was behind us, yet already we felt stuck in the seemingly endless turmoil of basic science classes. For many of my classmates, consumed by the selfless desire to see other human beings in pain and make them better, this was sending them into a lather. Sure, asking meaningless questions throughout and after each lecture in the hopes the visiting-adjunct-clinical-assistant professor would remember them when it came time to assign grades was fulfilling. But if they didn't start seeing some real people in need of their vast healing powers soon, they were going to explode.

Fortunately, the folks on the curriculum committee anticipated this frenzied lust for real, treatable patients. This, combined with their desire to remain an accredited school of medicine, encouraged the committee to give Primary Care— a department free of any petty insecurities which might arise from the fact that because they don't get to do any vital Medicare-covered procedures (such as wart removals or pupil dilations) and therefore don't really generate any money for the university—free rein over "patient interaction" instruction. Thus, Clinical Arts was born.

Clinical Arts, our sensitive instructors cooed, would give us "early exposure" to clinical medicine. We would obtain this by interviewing a "standardized patient-actor" once a month and spending the rest of the time looking up information related to the "patient's" fictional disease. This didn't sound particularly clinical to me, but I figured they must know what they're doing—after all, they are primary care physicians.

On the first day, an actor to be interviewed was ushered into the room. The next three hours seemed to go by in slow motion. The student interviewer, armed with one week's knowledge of biochemistry and genetics, introduced himself and then sat transfixed, as if in the glare of oncoming headlights. The rest of us watched in stunned silence, unsure what to do other than perhaps draw the molecular structure of something or make a genetic family tree. The student looked at the patient/actor. The patient acted as if he was looking at the student. The attending, sensing he was losing control, handed a piece of paper to the student and announced that this listed the patient's vital signs taken by the nurse.

The student took the paper and stared at it with a look of complete confusion and distress. It would have been comical but for the fact that each second meant the loss of another chunk of the self-confidence it had taken him a lifetime to build. Finally, in a voice saturated with the kind of helpless defeat felt by pole vaulters who have just discovered that their country will skip the Olympics, he asked the instructor, "What do these numbers mean?"

The instructor, not part of the "role play," sensitively shrugged his shoulders and remained silent. Mercifully, the student remembered he could call a "time-out" when he needed help from the group and proceeded to do so with considerable fervor. For the next forty-five minutes, the attending very gently allowed the group to try to determine what the two numbers in the blood pressure reading meant, ignoring our desperate cries for him, our teacher, to tell us. After all, we pleaded, the meaning of "140/95" was not really a subject for debate. The attending, however, remained annoyingly, stupidly, silent.

The next two hours passed similarly, with the interviewer and the class, his "ectopic brain," trying to figure out, without ever having seen a doctor interview a patient, just what disease this actor had and how to treat it. At the end of three sweaty, nerve-shredding hours, we were amazed to discover that the patient had sickle cell disease—amazed, since only one out of nine of us had ever even heard of it.

Pleased with our progress, our teacher announced it was time to pick "learning issues." These were basic facts about sickle cell disease that we would each look up and report to the group the following week. He felt this would be a much more economical use of our time than using his years of medical training and experience to give us a short lecture on sickle cell disease highlighting the important facts and concepts. If he were to do that, he reassured us soothingly, there wouldn't be any discussion. Why this topic needed to be discussed by a bunch of people who didn't know anything about medicine was still beyond us.

My topic was the treatment of the disease. After class, I asked the attending if he would list some of the main treatments so that I could look up the details more easily.

"No," was his kindly answer, the kind of answer for which he was getting an extra $3,000 to teach this class.

"Why?" was the only word my amazed brain could muster.

"Because you need to look that up yourself," he countered cleverly. I imagined my own blood pressure was rising above "140/95."

"Isn't the purpose of this exercise to learn about sickle cell disease?" I asked, repressing my anger the way I used to before I cracked one night and went after lightning bugs with my whiffleball bat.

"Well, no, not really," he replied sensitively.

"If my purpose here isn't to learn the information, why do I have to spend my time finding and presenting it to everyone and then listening to the other students present their topics, which I also presumably don't have to learn?" I reasoned, wondering just where my whiffleball bat was.

"I think it would be a good experience to look it up," he said, as if speaking to some idiot who still didn't know how to look things up in the index of Harrison's. Then he walked away.

And so I was introduced to the evil design of Clinical Arts: to force us to spend two hours a week looking up topics that our instructor could have explained in about three minutes. It turns out that our teacher was correct: the purpose of Clinical Arts was not that we learn the actual medical information, but that we, twenty-something-year-old college graduates, learn how to find the information listed alphabetically in the index of Harrison's. Once we found the information, of course, it was still necessary to copy it word for word and then report it the following week in as mind-numbingly boring a fashion as possible. Without necessarily learning it.

Indisputably, my classmates and I have gotten our desperately needed "patient interaction" by weaving our way through fake clinical situations without any actual medical knowledge, much like a blind bird flying through an asteroid storm. And we've learned some valuable clinical pearls. For example, you can't ask a patient a question and expect a truthful answer. No, you have to drag it from him by asking it fifteen, sixteen, and sometimes even seventeen times before he grudgingly tells you that he really came to the clinic for his persistent cough, and not his arm pain, as he originally insisted. Moreover, you have to be very, very gentle with patients, since they are (apparently) apt to cry at any moment, even when asked to remove their shoes. And every patient has a secret to hide. Only by tricking each one into spilling it can a doctor be privy to their deep, hidden reasons for making an appointment.

Exactly what "Arts" we are learning I'm still not sure, though I'm certain that my newfound ability to sit for two hours and listen to my patient talk about her daughter's recipe for fried groundhog will prove invaluable once I'm on the wards. Until then, I'm attempting to learn some medical information from other sources so that when it's my turn to "interview," I'll actually know a little bit about medicine. Of course, the Primary Care department seems convinced that such knowledge isn't actually necessary for proper patient care. If the results of my first set of midterms are any indication, I sure hope they're right.

How Gross Is Anatomy?

Gross Anatomy. Those two words have come to symbolize a rite of passage for all medical students. It is the time when they become different from their non-medical peers, people who still play on the Internet all day and don't study ketogenesis on the weekends. It is their first brush with death, the first step toward learning how to preserve life. It is a move across a line that can't be re-crossed—the line that separates the outer world from the inner sanctum of the human body. And it is with trepidation that medical students everywhere face this somber prospect. Nonetheless, I was not afraid.

The first day of class, I made my way with a light heart to the basement of Obturator Hall, only to be met by a wall of smell that, while not compatible with life, was neither a signpost of death. It was an odor that issued from things kept from decomposing in a very, very artificial way, a smell that seemed to say, "Welcome to Purgatory! It's not so bad here! Grab a spleen!" I entered, unfazed.

And why be nervous? Hell, I'd seen the movies. The good-natured med student with the nice haircut always passed his anatomy class through hard work, gutsy decisions, and raw nerve. Sure, I'd heard about the grueling afternoons of dissection, of finding and memorizing every nerve, bone, and lymphatic. I knew about the instructors, pacing the room like white-coated panthers, ready to pounce on the unfortunate student who couldn't name the thirteen arteries that came off the inferior mesenteric. Me? I wasn't nervous.

I made my way to my table, which was covered by a lumpy plastic sheet. I got out my dissection kit, put on a pair of rubber gloves, and gathered with my fellow dissectors around the mass. I found myself hoping that it wasn't, in reality, a dead person. When we took off the plastic, however, there could be no question. She had all the parts a human being has, including a yellow motionless face whose expression seemed to say, "Just what are you planning to do with that knife? Let's just put it down and talk this out like adults." I felt a small chill, and then a larger one. Unable to meet her flaccid countenance, I turned away.

But then I thought, what would the stony-jawed med student in the movie do right now? Of course, he would wink at the female med student across the room in answer to her sultry gaze. But meeting with more gazes of horror and disgust than usual, I decided instead to volunteer to make the first incision. I took a deep breath, mustering all my courage. Placing the scalpel on the jaundiced, waxy skin, I closed my eyes and cut slowly and evenly right down the middle.

There was a moment of silence from the other group members. As I stood there, eyes still closed, I felt the significance of what had just happened. Myths of the sacredness of the human body go back to the beginning of humanity. The body is the one possession each person can unquestionably call her own. By opening this one, we were witnessing the single most personal thing this woman had, in life and in death. This was the kind of responsibility a doctor took on; this was what was meant by the sanctity of the physician-patient relationship, something to be cherished and never taken lightly. We were in this together now and we couldn't go back. It seemed that for the first time, we were on our way to becoming doctors. I sensed the five students around me immersed in similar contemplation as we stood silently. We were learning a valuable lesson. I opened my eyes.

"Maybe you should actually cut through the skin?" one of my compatriots suggested, breaking what was not as thoughtful a silence as I had imagined. Another, in not quite as philosophical a mood as I had believed, suggested using the sharp part of the blade. Yet another, who didn't seem a bit overwhelmed, asked if maybe I'd like to use two hands. Indeed, looking down at the patient's back, I noticed a long, shallow depression in the otherwise-intact yellow skin. I excused myself and went for a very long drink of water.

It was downhill from there.

After several weeks of picking fascia off bones and doing crossword puzzles, Gross Anatomy became as mundane as any other class. Within days, our concept of the woman as an actual person became merely a distant thought as we leaned our elbows on her face to get a better angle while dissecting her lungs. Her organs were, well, just organs—to be studied and then placed in a plastic bag and kept moist. And so, Gross Anatomy taught me another important lesson: If you don't keep your distance from a situation, you can't be effective in what you do. If you get caught up in every medical encounter, you'll be worthless as a doctor.

But, after I had begun with so much confidence, I now found my faith shaken. I was, I had to admit for the first time, a bit nervous. Because I had learned something else in those first few days—a lesson as terrible as it was true. I had learned that apparently, you can't always believe everything you see in the movies.

One day, I was spending my spare time in the history of medicine room in the library's basement, as I often do, when a thought occurred to me: Dr. Seuss, creator of my favorite childhood books, was a doctor, was he not? What if he had written his well-known stories, read by children across the world, for the medical literature? Inspired by Dr. Seuss, I have written the poems scattered throughout this book. "The Lorax" was my model for this one.

The Thorax

There once was an old man
With lungs nearly dead,
And one day a voice spoke to him.
Here is what it said:

My name is The Thorax.
I speak for the Bronchial Trees.
I ask you not to smoke now.
I ask you now, please!

But the man grabbed some paper
Filled with tobacco and tar.
He lit it on fire, thinking
"What a fine thing you are!"

The Lungs began to shiver.
The Cilia started to shake.
What Alveoli were left
Thought this a big mistake.

As the man prepared to inhale
And fill his lungs with smoke,
A little voice rose to his ears
And this is what it spoke:

My name is The Thorax.
I speak for the Bronchial Trees.
I ask you not to smoke now.
You will give us disease!

But the man didn't listen,
He prepared to breathe in.
And The Thorax then saw
All this carcinogen.

And he knew what would happen.
All the Cells it would char.
All those happy Bronchi
Covered up with tar.

No, No, NO! He spoke up.
He let out a call.
No, No, NO! Once again,
You will soon kill us all!

My name is The Thorax!
I speak for the Bronchial Trees!
Dear sir, do not hurt us!
Oh do not, sir, please!

These cells are fragile!
The Parenchyma too!
I beg to you sir,
This is a bad thing to do!

The man just paused briefly,
Then continued his act.
He inhaled the smoke deeply
And his lungs loudly hacked.

A thin voice arose . . .

My name is The Thorax
And I'll speak no more.
For there is no longer
Anything to speak for.

The Surfactant is gone.
The Cells are all dead.
We are no longer viable.
There's no more to be said.

We Hold These Truths To Be Cell(f)-Evident

There's a big scam going on in medical school. It has, thus far, gone undetected, insidiously hidden in a place no one thinks to look—the first-year curriculum. This is a scam so old and so well entrenched that it has become as much a part of medical education as the Krebs cycle and the genetics professors unable to deliver an organized lecture on the insignificant piece of research they've spent their entire lives pursuing. This scam has been passed down, unchallenged, in medical training for more than two centuries. It is Cell Biology.

Having looked this boil in the dome and lanced it, I now feel it is my duty to expose it and bring it to its dermis. This ancient fraud involves looking through tiny holes at blurry, unrecognizable dots and smudges, while being told that information can, somehow, be gained from these shapeless specks. It takes up hours of our time and gives us only heartbreak and misery in return, covering our lab in a sea of hematoxylin-stained tears.

But why, you and every dogma-spewing microanatomy lackey might ask, is this a scam? After all, if you cut a piece of tissue thin enough, place it on a slide, and use powerful lights and lenses to make it appear larger, should you not be able to discern the microscopic processes that take place within the body? Shouldn't you, at least, be able to see the individual cells?

But that's just the thing. You can't see cells, but not because the lenses aren't powerful enough or the lights aren't the correct wavelength. The reason is simple, and the impetus behind an upcoming paper I plan to present to The Literature as a beacon of truth for medical students and instructors alike. Sure, at first I was like the rest of the herd. I sat at my microscope, searching my numbered slides in vain for whatever crazy thing the syllabus directed. I would move from 4x to 10x to 40x with the dexterity of a wounded moose, sometimes even putting oil on my slide with the hope of catching a glimpse of something at "100x." But always there were just dots and mushy things clumped in no discernible pattern.

During those long, frustrating hours, I had time to think. And the more I thought, the clearer it became—there is no such thing as a cell.

Now, many will counter that people see cells in their electron microscopes every day. *That's what they want you to believe.* If you've ever looked at an electron micrograph, you know that all you see are grainy, squiggly lines. Indeed, the only way you know you've got a "Golgi apparatus" or a "smooth endoplasmic reticulum" is because the textbook editor has placed a big black "G" or "SER" in the middle of some grainy, squiggly lines. And they've done it because they're part of the scam; they purchased an electron microscope for $267,334 and lost the receipt. So they have no choice but to fill up books with pages of blurry pictures. (If anyone can explain how a bunch of dials and vacuum tubes makes tiny little cells look really big, I'd like to hear it. Maybe they would also explain The Bermuda Triangle, The Loch Ness Monster, and "antibiotics" while they're at it.)

Furthermore, look at the stuff they're trying to teach us. Has anyone ever really seen a Reed-Sternberg cell? And what the hell is a "PALS"? Sure, they've assigned a lot of big fancy names to things, enshrined within rules that they hand down as gospel, and, for years, everyone has believed. But why? When I look around the lab, I see people playing with dials hoping to see a "multinucleated giant cell." After about forty-five minutes, they're going to give up, say they saw one, and move on. Heck, it's what I do. I'm not interested in spending valuable nap time trying to differentiate the jejunum from the ileum based on the number of "goblet cells." Because, as it turns out, there is no difference.

Besides, a lot of people have their livelihoods at stake and they're willing to lie to keep them. If you had spent thirteen lonely years learning to be a pathologist, would you tell anyone there was no such thing as a cell, even if you knew? Or would you perpetuate the myth by trying to show a bunch of impressionable kids that there really are "sinusoids" in liver tissue? The day pathologists can no longer convince people of the existence of periarticular bone growth is the day they have to start doing nothing but autopsies. And for a pathologist, even that is too much human interaction to bear.

But, you ask, if my theory is true (as is now overwhelmingly apparent), then what do I propose in place of these fictional cells? I can name the substance in one word: Phlegm.

Yes, our Greek ancestors, as in their architecture, art, and love of plazas, were far beyond us in their understanding of medicine. Two thousand five hundred years ago, without the aid of fancy instruments or Christianity, the Greeks developed the simple, unifying concept of the four types of Phlegm. I speak here not just of the oozy stuff that drips from our noses, but of much more. Yellow. Red. Green. Black. The four colors of Phlegm. When in balance, Phlegm kept a person healthy in the ancient world and, although many of us fail to recognize this, it still does today.

Why have we forsaken the wisdom of our past? Because medicine, like it or not, is a big business. As long as there is a cell-based theory of medicine, there will be drug companies, surgical instrument manufacturers, and physician assistants all making zillions of dollars. Return to the Phlegm-based model and suddenly the field is not so lucrative. For example, a man cuts himself and loses a couple units of blood—suddenly he's a little low on Red Phlegm. Had we heeded the sage advice of Vesicles, we might be able to pull up to the Red pump at something like a gas station and bring the patient into balance. But instead, we waste our resources first finding blood that matches and that has been extensively screened for any viruses, factor deficiencies, and diseases, and then using antibody-driven tests to prevent rejection. Such a waste of time and money, but what a fantastic way for third parties to make a profit!

To conclude on a positive note, I do believe there is hope for the future of medicine. Indeed, a new Golden Age may soon be upon us, as more people heed the message of the Ancients and embrace the concept of Phlegm. This is particularly timely. As cost becomes the primary concern, one cannot help but realize the importance of eliminating all superfluous technology based upon the "cellular concept" of medicine. Except, of course, in the case of hopelessly doomed people maintained on ventilators for months or years at a cost of millions of taxpayers' dollars because doctors can't turn the machine off without being prosecuted for murder.

This new Age has to start somewhere. And it is in the idealistic doctors of the future that the seeds must be planted. It is my firm conviction that to accomplish this, cell biology classes must quickly become a thing of the past. As each medical school drops this from its curriculum, a hundred fewer medical students will be led astray. I, for one, plan to play my part in this Great Transformation by never attending a cell biology lab session again.

Localize Your Own Lesions

Localize the lesion.

I am haunted by these words.

After a month of neurology—a month filled with more stenosis and demyelination than I ever thought possible—I've begun having dreams. The landscape of my dreams is a hazy, vaguely familiar place filled with characters I've grown to recognize in the way one would a seldom-seen acquaintance. There's the smooth easiness of the midbrain; the glib, flashy parietal lobe of the cortex; the raging fire and brimstone of the amygdala; the cold certainty of the pons.

As I interact with these entities I grow more confused and frustrated. I know that there's something wrong and I can fix it, if only I can get to that right place, find that hidden amyloid plaque. But sadly, glial and neuronal cells alike mock me as I trudge through the wasteland of the lower temporal lobe. I cross the midline countless times, never reaching my goal.

Within these dreams I have visions I cannot fully explain: up-going toes and left-sided neglect, agraphesthesia and dysphagia. Is it a problem of production, or of comprehension? Every night, no matter how many ganglia I pass through, the puzzle remains unsolved.

When will these dreams end? How many more nights before I'm able to grasp that neurofibrillary tangle by both ends and pull it straight? All I know is that when I sleep the entire night without a single lacunar embolus, I'll finally have won. And when the sun rises that morning, the dark mysterious world of neurology will be a thing of the past. But by then I'll probably already have failed the final.

Bugs' Prey

I thought I understood medicine fairly well. After all, I had made it through the first three blocks of first-year classes with, if not exactly *flying* colors, then, well, at least colors. So now, in the fourth block, all I can do is close my eyes and wonder: What went wrong?

I had learned a lot of important things during the first months of med school. I'd learned the four uses of ketones, the names of all 387 blood vessels in the forearm, and that every nerve in the body goes through the basal ganglia. But perhaps the most important thing I had learned was that, without exception, everything you need to know for the tests is contained in the lecture handouts. Which is why, when it came time for the first microbiology test, I figured I would just continue my previously successful study regimen of looking over the handouts and then watching basketball. How could I go wrong?

Now, many believe that had I been capable of waking up in time for the 8:00 A.M. lecture every morning, much of what you're about to read would never have happened. Some think that had I attended lab even once, I never would have become the withered shell of a med student that I am today. Some even suggest that had I bought the textbook, I would not be in the straits I currently find myself in. But these are theories which, sadly, we will never have the chance to disprove. For what happened has happened and all I can do now is try to pick up the pieces. So that's what I'm doing right now—slowly, gradually, picking up the pieces.

You may ask, "What could possibly have happened during this midterm to cause such damage?" I think it would be therapeutic for me to tell you.

As I walked into the test room that black day, I was feeling pretty good. The year was three-fourths over and I had made it through fairly unscathed, except for my new facial tic and the inability to carry on a conversation without occasional episodes of sobbing. And, with medication, the dreams have subsided; in fact, many nights I can sleep three or four hours straight before being awakened by images of falling off the down-slope of a Frank-Starling curve or being caught between the waves of a Cheyne-Stokes breathing pattern. Yes, I was feeling good as I took my place at the desk and prepared myself for this latest battle.

As I sat there, I reflected upon the last three days. I had begun without a single ounce of knowledge about microbiology. Bacteria, as far as I was concerned, were just things that grew in, and eventually overtook, my shower stall. That there were different kinds with different capsules, different methods of virility, and different places they liked to live were ideas as foreign to me as the concept that my fellow students purposely woke up at 7 A.M. just to listen to someone lecture about all that stuff.

I went to the library, found a quiet place, and began to study. I carefully put the 35 lecture handouts, in order, in a neat stack and picked up Lecture 1, on gram-positive Staphylococci. I had heard of those. I memorized the different kinds, where they were found, the path through which each entered the body, the diseases they caused, the symptoms of infection, their preferred culture media, the common host responses, and the antibiotics used to fight them. This wouldn't be hard—after all, foregoing understanding of the material in favor of pure memorization had gotten me this far in life, why should it fail me now? On to Lecture 2.

Gram-positive Streptococci. Well, there are a few more of those. But they posed no problem. I'd just memorize the same stuff for groups A through D and the irregular strains and then learn how to differentiate them, both across and within groups. Ninety minutes later, the information was all packed away in some neurons I had been saving for baseball statistics. I was ready for Lecture 3.

Gram-positive Bacilli. I didn't know they existed. Well, just keep on plowing through, I figured. So I did. Then I plowed through the Gram-negatives: *Salmonella, Shigella, Proteus, Yersinia, Brucella, and Klebsiella.* By now, it was late. I had packed the facts in tighter and tighter and was starting to feel as if some were slipping out. Time for a little self-test to see if I was keeping everything straight. Needless to say, I wasn't. Best to sleep on it, I reasoned, and begin again when I was rested.

The next day I re-memorized all the facts I'd crammed in the day before. The names of the different microbes and agars and diseases were starting to run together. I made charts. I drew diagrams. I compiled lists. I grew tired and filled up on soda. I napped, awoke, and drank coffee. I developed atrial fibrillation and, shaken, went to sleep.

Day 3 dawned—the day before the midterm. There were still more bugs to learn. I tried, but each new piece of information knocked out another one that had been only tenuously balanced upon a hippocampal dendrite. I couldn't seem to stuff in any more facts. But I persisted with the kind of dedication that allows people who aren't very smart to succeed beyond their normal capabilities. And, slowly, I felt it all sinking in. Now granted, I didn't feel I had an overall picture, the way I did of, say, the 1978 American League pennant race. But I was beginning to feel that I could keep the facts straight, that I could hold it all together long enough to spill it on the pages of my midterm the next day. I fluffed up my pillow, put plugs in my ears, and went to sleep.

The next morning, relatively confident, I sat at my desk. Because there was so much material to learn, I figured everyone else must have had the same troubles that I did, and we couldn't possibly be expected to know it all anyway. The test began.

There are times in life when a person knows that he truly grasps a concept, when he feels he can provide a reasonable answer for any question flung at him. He seems almost in a trance; the concept is not so much something he has learned as it is a part of him. When this happens, he can throw his shoulders back, allow his arms to dangle at his sides, and truly relax, comforted by the knowledge that he has finally achieved success. This, however, was not one of those times.

The midterm contained, I will admit, many familiar words. Some words, in fact, I could even define. But I could not, under any circumstances, answer a single question. I tried, but they were devastating: Which bacteria enter through cracks in the foot when you walk through Chinese water chestnut fields? What causes *E. coli* to proliferate in the colon? Which grows on McConkey's agar? Which is motile, and which is carried in the stomach of Tsetse flies? Which has a glycoprotein capsule, and which does not? The questions flew at me like a hundred species of birds—I recognized many, but couldn't actually name even one.

I began to sweat. I entertained visions of sticking my finger in an electrical outlet. I couldn't think at all. For three hours I sat there, my fluid losses nearly forcing me to request an IV. And then it was over. Unsure how to react—I had never failed a test before—I went home and fell asleep.

As it turned out, I didn't quite fail—although I came pretty darned close. It was, I admit, a little scary. But, fortunately, the entire experience taught me some valuable lessons. I learned, for instance, that mastering such a voluminous subject requires organization and preparedness. I also learned that memorizing things really only provides one with a loose set of connections and cannot replace actually learning and understanding the material. But most importantly, I learned that if I ever have a patient with any sort of infection whatsoever, I'm immediately getting an Infectious Diseases consult.

Road Warrior

Last night I was driving down Highway 15-501, thinking about studying for my upcoming pathology exam, when a car about 300 yards ahead of me suddenly flipped over. Everybody came to a stop. The police quickly arrived on the scene and helped the driver out of her overturned car.

Concerned in the way any normal, non-medically trained person would be, I sat and waited—until I heard a knock on my window.

"Hey, you're a medical student, right?" Unsure who this person was, I nodded dumbly. "Well, shouldn't you go help that girl or something? There's no ambulance here. Just, like, check her out or something?" Afraid to admit that my medical knowledge included only a few isolated steps from the fatty acid cycle, I nodded dumbly once again.

Then I thought: this could be my first chance to do something real, to show society that one day I could become a successful doctor, despite what any complex battery of tests and lengthy psychoanalysis said. Fortunately, my bag from school was behind the seat. I grabbed my ophthalmoscope, my reflex hammer, and both my 128-Hz and 512-Hz tuning forks, and set out through the rows of cars to where the girl was sitting.

After waiting several minutes to be invited to do an extended ENT exam, I was finally noticed. "Can I help you?" the policeman asked in the tone of voice of someone who knew that I could not help. Several responses floated through my head, many of which did not sound as lame as "Um, I'm a medical student, sir."

Obviously, the policeman had dealt with first-year medical students before, because my proclamation didn't seem to mean anything to him other than that maybe, if I started to get out of line, he could shoot me. So I continued.

"I'm a medical student," I repeated, letting the full weight of my weeks of studying genetics sink in. "Can I do anything to help?"

The policeman did not look like he thought I could do anything to help. But apparently having nothing better to do until the people who did know how to help arrived, he gestured toward the girl in a manner I could only assume meant "make sure you check her back for fremitus too." I eagerly went to work.

19

The hardest part was fighting against my Clinical Arts training, which told me to ask the girl what had brought her here today. I didn't know how to handle a patient whose problem did not need to be dragged out of her by repeating the same question thirteen times. Unable to call a "time out," however, I began my exam.

I closed my eyes until the list of "things to do on a physical exam" materialized in front of me. After examining her scalp closely for moles or any other discoloration, I moved next to her HEENT. Her sclerae were non-icteric, her Weber test localized better to bone than to air, and her oral cavity showed no evidence of thrush. I was just preparing to check whether her thyroid was midline when she spoke.

"What the hell are you doing?" she asked. I had thought it was pretty obvious. Perhaps she was having mental status changes.

"Spell 'world' backwards," I suggested gently, but it was too late. She had started to walk away. Fearing that I was losing control of the situation, I produced my ophthalmoscope. A medical instrument, I reasoned, could only enhance her respect for my medical acumen.

Once I put the ophthalmoscope to her eyes, I realized that first, I didn't know what I could possibly see on her fundus that would alert me to any problems caused by the accident, and second, I didn't really know how to use the ophthalmoscope anyway. So I stood there, shining and grunting, unable to see anything but happy that the patient was allowing me to look. Finally, satisfied that if she did indeed have a retina, it was intact, I removed my face from hers (to her obvious relief) and proceeded to stand there, desperately wondering what to do next. Listen for murmurs? Do a gynecological exam? I was explaining that she needed to lie on the ground for a moment so that I could feel for hepatosplenomegaly when the whine of a siren rescued us both.

One of the paramedics climbed out of the ambulance, saw me with my ophthalmoscope, and asked me for the "bullet."

"The what?" I cleverly responded, wondering if I should check for lymph node enlargement.

"What's going on with her?" he asked, waiting for the information necessary to care for her during her ride to the Emergency Department.

"Oh. Sure. Um, car accident." I was clearly in control now. "Yeah. Car accident."

"How are her pupils? What kind of breathing pattern does she have?" These questions seemed reasonable in that they sounded medical. But I wasn't sure why they were relevant. Well, I was the doctor-to-be here. I wasn't going to let some paramedic tell me what was relevant.

"Oh, I didn't check those. But she's in regular rate and rhythm."

The paramedic called back into the ambulance. "Dan, I'm gonna be a minute. Gotta do a quick exam." I was losing control of the situation again.

I stood there quietly for the next five minutes as the paramedic showed me how to do a physical exam on a person who has just been in a car accident. As I suspected, no gynecological exam was necessary.

While the patient was being loaded into the ambulance, I quietly stepped away from the scene and walked back toward my car. As I did, people started leaning out of their windows, thanking me and telling me that what I had just done was great. I tried to explain that I didn't actually do anything, that the closest I came to affecting the outcome was nearly poking the girl's eye out with my ophthalmoscope. But, strangely, no one would listen to me. I realized that they felt secure just knowing that there was a "doctor" there, whether I did anything or not.

That day I learned that there is more to being a doctor than accurate diagnoses and successful treatments. People would expect things of me and, whether those expectations were reasonable or not, it would be my responsibility to try to live up to them. As I made my way home, the whole thing seemed overwhelming. But then it dawned on me that no matter how little I understood about medicine, lay people would still listen to me, simply by virtue of my title. I thought about that a little bit more. Suddenly, I smiled. Learning all that pathology for my test didn't seem nearly as important anymore.

"The Cat in the Hat" by Dr. Seuss is a classic tale. My version should, I believe, appear in the *American Journal of Cardiology*.

The Cad In The Dad

Good day, sir.
Good day, sir.
Step right this way, sir.
You say you've had chest pain
Everyday since last May, sir?

Come right this way,
Sit down on this table.
Show me where this pain
Makes you hurt, if you're able.

You point to your arm!
You point to your chest!
And you say that this happens
Even at rest?

You become quite nauseous
And then start to sweat.
You get short of breath
And this all makes you fret?

You've smoked all your life
And you have hypertension,
You're morbidly obese
(Which goes without mention)?

Your father has passed on,
A brother is not alive.
They both had infarctions
Before age forty-five?

Then we'll send you to echo,
And then a stress-test!
A barium swallow
While we x-ray your chest!

Oh, this doesn't look good.
I see left main disease,
But I know we can treat it.
I'll explain, if you please.

We can treat you with CABG.
We can treat you with plasty.
We can treat you with stents,
Though that could get nasty

So, take your time, go decide;
Even talk to your wife.
We don't want you to die
In the prime of your life.

But remember, no more fat,
No more smoking or booze.
After all, it's your life
That you now stand to lose!

What is this? You say what?
That you cannot comply?
That you cannot stop smoking?
That you cannot even try?

That you must eat your bacon
And your six-pack of beer?
That you need these things more
Than this life you hold dear?

Then good bye, sir.
Good bye, sir.
You are making me cry, sir.
I'll be happy to help
When you're willing to try, sir.

23

My Café Au Lait Spot

Over the years, I've heard a lot of talk from fellow students about coffee—how they need it, how they can't live without it, how they can't wake up in the morning until they've licked every last grainy, smelly drop out of the bottom of their three-liter coffee machines. Not having much coffee experience, I had to take their word for it. Well, there *was* the liter and a half I drank before the MCAT, rendering myself unable to fill in those microscopic scantron answer spaces.

My next encounter involved drinking three ounces of coffee (and about fourteen ounces of milk) at 4 A.M. before last year's biochemistry final, resulting in a reentry tachycardia of about 230 beats per minute. It was all my roommate could do to restrain me from ripping my heart out of my rib cage with a bread knife and stomping on it until it resumed a normal sinus rhythm (sort of like the open-chest cardiac massage they used before external defibrillation was invented).

So, for a time, I was deathly afraid of coffee. But just as the flashbacks had diminished to once a week, the Yuppee Espresso Stand (Y.E.S.) appeared in the hospital cafeteria. Once I had gained enough courage to go near it, I saw that it advertised all sorts of yummy-sounding things. How could a mocha-cherry-cinnamon double-iced cappuccino be bad? Who wouldn't drool over a tall whipped vanilla-nut latte with fudge-almond cream? These things must be good, I reasoned, because (a) while I had no idea what they were, I imagined tall, attractive people wearing black turtlenecks did; and (b) at least three pieces of American paper currency were necessary to buy one.

Though I didn't partake of coffee, I now found myself considering it, attributing my earlier "bad trips" to impurities in the beans or a bad mixing job. And when my physical diagnosis attending suggested that we go down to the cafeteria to get some coffee and talk about our patients, I was secretly thrilled. I finally had an excuse to get a Triple Karamel Kreme Kappuccino, and no one could stop me.

When we got downstairs, my eyes zeroed in on the pretty colors and smiling faces of the Y.E.S. At the counter, my attending ordered a Cappuccino Grande.

24

Wow! I didn't even know they made something like that: I mean, not only was it Cappuccino—it was Grande. It sounded like the Zeus of trendy drinks, so I ordered one as well. My attending handed over the $23.96, and I watched as he sprinkled some cocoa on top of his frothy steamed milk. I did the same, excited at the prospect of finally joining the Coffee Generation. We found a table and my attending began talking about lymphoma or something, but I couldn't hear a word—I was too busy inhaling the sweet, creamy aroma of my Cappuccino Grande. Finally, unable to wait any longer, I closed my eyes, raised the cup to my lips, and drank deeply, envisioning the silky taste of warm coffee ice cream that was to come.

It tasted like . . . coffee. Which tastes . . . bad.

I hadn't been so disappointed since the Cleveland Cavaliers traded Ron Harper. *This* was what 17 percent of the Gross National Product is spent on? *This* was what everybody on my rotation couldn't stop droning on about in that glassy-eyed, drool-flecked way coffee drinkers have when they feel they're in a situation so utterly stressful and malignant that the only coping mechanism available to their worn and tortured bodies is their ability to metabolize xanthines?

At first I thought I was in one of those commercials where they replaced the *Folger's* crystals with dirt. I felt duped, tricked by society. Like when everyone keeps telling me "Layla" is one of the greatest songs of all time or that it's possible to learn the renal system. It took all my willpower to drink the entire Colombian monstrosity, an act inevitably followed by that whole atrial-fibrillation thing. But by then I didn't care—once again, I had been savagely mocked by the same world I've tried so hard to fit into. And besides, the only utensils within reach were those dull plastic knives.

Neurosurgery Made Simplistic

With the ever-increasing cost of health care, it has become imperative to "trim the fat" as much as possible. Measures such as decreased lengths of hospital stays, consolidation of services and staff, and shorter times per clinic visit have gone a long way toward keeping hospitals financially viable in today's competitive health care market.

One of the most successful innovations has been the advent of the nurse practitioner. Overnight, a nurse trained for routine patient care and support tasks mysteriously becomes certified to perform the same job as a physician who completes four years of medical school and a lengthy, rigorous residency. Because nurse practitioners work for only fifteen-sixteenths of a doctor's salary, more and more hospitals are finding these employees so cost-efficient that they overlook the fact that they never learned such trivial things as physiology.

Certainly, the use of nurse practitioners has flourished in areas such as anesthesiology, family practice, and obstetrics, rendering physicians in these fields nearly obsolete other than as the sole person legally liable for everything a nurse practitioner does. And unless something crazy like a complication requiring actual medical training occurs, a nurse practitioner's performance is more or less equal to that of their physician counterpart.

As not only a future health care provider but also a consumer, I am as interested as anyone in making tomorrow's medicine, if not safer, then at least cheaper. Which is why, this spring, I will embark upon my latest, and perhaps most promising, venture. I will unveil the Jeff Drayer Program for Neurosurgery Nurse Practitioners.

As we all know, brain surgery can be an expensive ordeal. Medicaid pays not only for the operating room, supplies, and ancillary personnel, but also for a surgeon with up to ten years of training *after* medical school. Imagine the savings if we only had to pay for someone with just two years of undergraduate schooling and an additional year in my program!

What will I teach? Well, since all knowledge of the body other than the nervous system will be superfluous, the other six systems can be ignored. After a thorough study of "Neuroanatomy Made Ridiculously Simple," a three-hour session on tying knots, and watching a video on skull-cracking, the rest of the training will occur "in the field," where students will "learn by doing." This involves first-assisting during and then actually performing basic neurosurgical procedures under the supervision of either a neurosurgeon or a neurosurgery nurse practitioner. After all, what do neurosurgery residents really learn during their 110-hour weeks in their decade-long residency? Just the same few basic procedures that make up 95 percent of their profession's work. How many times does someone really need to do each procedure before going it alone? (Don't forget, my program isn't for just anyone—each student must first complete at least two years in an accredited nursing program, often during their late teens, learning how to start IVs, hang antibiotics, and measure respiration rates.)

After successfully completing one of each of the main types of surgery (or two partially successful completions), students will be ready to work for major hospitals, where they can cheaply replace several of the current surgeons, some of whom are making more than $150,000 a year! The benefits for the MBAs and insurance actuaries running the hospital are clear.

Once my program begins, I believe we will ride the train of financial stability into the next century. Eventually, people will forget that some diseases were once treatable, and the days when people with aneurysms didn't die will soon become a hazy memory. Our children and grandchildren will think of death by brainstem herniation as one of those inevitable facts of life, just like upper respiratory infections, stomachaches, and the occasional fatal hemorrhage at midwife-assisted births.

And once that happens, everyone wins! Nurses would get the chance to do things that used to require a lot of bothersome education and pesky training and still get to leave the hospital at exactly five o'clock, no matter what kind of case they happened to be treating. Hospitals would save an enormous amount of money not only on salaries, but also in areas such as post-op and follow-up care. Patients would still go to their surgeries assured that one M.D. trained in neurosurgery is somewhere in the hospital or, at least, close by on beeper call. And, doctors, no longer particularly necessary, would not have to do those tedious sixteen-hour surgeries that they trained their entire lives for.

Yes, medicine is facing a time of great change. Visionaries such as myself must take it upon ourselves to step up and lead this struggling field back into prosperity. It won't be easy, and sacrifices will have to be made. But until every HMO's CEO has his very own Learjet, we, as tomorrow's leaders, will have to buckle down and forge bravely ahead into the next century.

BOOK TWO

The Cost-Effective Use Of Leeches

I Don't Think I Know Anything

MS-II. Second-year medical student—how strange that sounds. When we arrived here last August and met our big sibs (the students in the class ahead of us charged with making sure we didn't fall on our scalpels in despair), we viewed them as giants, much more learned and wise than ourselves. Now, finding myself in the same position, I realize just how wrong we were. I know I don't speak for everyone in my class, but I, for one, will say this: I don't think I know anything.

Of course, some people might say that you may feel like that now, but you have learned more than you think. That is where they're wrong. I've lived with myself all year, have accurately assessed the amount of medical stuff I've learned, and have come to the realization that if first year were a gymnastics meet, the Romanian judge would have given me a 3.1.

I blame my lack of knowledge on the microbiology professors for scheduling their lectures at the unattendable hour of 8:00 A.M. I blame the pathology professors for teaching us that nausea and vomiting are the main symptoms for every disease. I even blame the genetics department for never teaching us how to make a chimeric mouse. It might seem as if I am projecting blame onto these people to cover up my own first-year failings. But I don't think so.

Nevertheless, first year is over, assuming the Pharmacology department's threats to make me retake their class were indeed idle. So, these days, the big question on many of my classmates' minds is "Just what goes on during second year?" When my family asks, I tell them that I'll be like Carter on *ER*. That always makes them happy and, for a while, it satisfied me too.

But unanswered questions remain, clogging those very synapses I should use to remember to check the inguinal nodes during lower extremity inspections. Questions such as, "What exactly does it mean to be 'on call'?" I've asked about fifty people and gotten thirty-eight different answers, many containing the word "awake." Will I be in the hospital all night? Will I have a beeper? Will I have to know anything from that class we took about the chemical pathways and stuff? I can't seem to get straight answers to any of these questions, and it's making me suspicious. Almost as suspicious as when my preceptor kept telling me to listen to heart sounds that obviously weren't there.

And now I'm being entrusted with a little sib of my own. It will be my turn to give more advice than anyone ever wanted about anything I feel like, and she'll have to listen because I have her test file. I'll encourage my little sib to look carefully through my tests from last year, not to glean intricate details from my essays, but rather to note the little apologies I scribbled beside them. What apologies, you ask? The ones assuring my sib-to-be that number four was a bad question, and we didn't even cover number eleven in class, and nobody but Aamer got number fourteen right so look at his damn test file if you want the right answer.

I always felt as if I was taking my tests in front of an audience and my answers were being shown on a big screen. Sort of like a game show where the only goal was to get about 60 percent of the questions right, and whose only prize was to finally get to leave the room so you didn't have to hear the guy in the corner eating yogurt. After every test, I always imagined a bunch of first-years gathered around my graded exam, mocking my ignorance of the fourth step of folate metabolism.

I know I'm going to give lots of advice that will be ignored. My little sib will still lug a bone box back to her apartment. She'll insist on buying a genetics textbook. She'll still try to learn the renal system. I suppose we all have to learn from our own mistakes. Everyone comes to King Med feeling like they own the world. But, as a famous person once said, it's only after we start learning lots of things that we realize just how much we don't know. Perhaps that's why I feel as if I don't know anything. Or maybe it's because I never attended microbiology class.

The Orient(ation) Express

Ah, orientation. One hundred new young faces from one hundred cities we can't remember, graduates of one hundred colleges we can't keep straight. And let me tell you, we oriented the hell out of them.

Yes, following the medical school tradition of doing much more than we should in less time than exists,[1] we held orientation week. After keeping the first-years out until 3 A.M. and then beginning the day with a meeting at eight, I stood in front of my afternoon tour group and looked upon their pale, haggard faces. I was reminded of the look that cartoon characters have when they're stranded on an island and begin to imagine their companions are big hot dogs. And who wouldn't look exhausted? They had just been through the most grueling five hours they'll experience until the lecture series on lipoproteins. Bus schedules! Public safety! Parking garage rules! It's overwhelming. But I dragged them through the tour anyway, with such medically relevant stops as the basketball stadium and the view from the ninth floor of the hospital. I even asked directions to the student lounge so we could experience our first look at the three couches and the television, which they won't see again for over a year.[2] Finally, I let them go only because it was time to get ready for a marathon dinner, at which they would be forced to swallow not only some potentially awful Mexican food but also three hours of unsolicited advice.

This went on all week until, finally, the weekend arrived. Time to relax? I don't think so. The first-years were up at nine for Sports Day so that they could soak up the ninety-five-degree sunshine and shave away their knees on the artificial turf. Sent 'em home for a quick nap and then it was on to a night of pool, greasy food, and line dancing. Sunday was filled with service projects, many involving sharp objects, and a picnic. This ended mercifully at sundown, so that the newly oriented MS-Is could tend to their wounded and get a little sleep. And they'd better, because class starts early Monday morning. It's funny; I could never remember why I took so many afternoon naps during first block. Now it comes flooding back—I was recovering from orientation week.

Orientation as an MS-II is very different. There's no pressure to remember everyone's name. There's no need to be at every event from start to finish. I finally think the slide show is funny. The only thing that has remained the same is that I still don't recognize a single name when someone lists the undergraduates they knew at Cornell.

But most of all, orientation as a second-year is *fun*. I've got a hundred friends in my class and, although we see each other throughout the year, who knows when we'll all be together again. There's really nowhere else for us to gather now that the amphitheater is taken over by a new horde of students, and too many people will be in surgery or in bed to have this kind of party. Besides, King Med is paying for the pizza.

Orientation, in the end, reminds me of putting pledges through a fraternity initiation. Inundating them with things to remember. Giving them a thousand tasks to accomplish. Placing them in new and disorienting settings. Making them so tired they can barely think, and then planting sinister thoughts in their minds, such as that it's possible to learn the renal system.

Every stage of the medical profession—from pre-med to med student to intern to resident to attending—involves working hard and performing well so that you can be accepted into the next group. You don't always understand the purpose of the things you're forced to do, but you do them anyway. You trust that each step has a reason and that if you don't know the reason at the time, it will become apparent eventually.

Orientation is hard and it's tiring but when it finally draws to a close, each new recruit will sit on their bed and think back over the past few days. And there will be a big grin on every face because, after all the pre-med classes, the applications, and the interviews, they've finally made it—they all belong to that next group.

Little do they know it's about to start all over again.

1. Unless we were to bend space.
2. We can't bend space.

The Death Of Clinical Arts
("So, How Does Being Dead Make You Feel?")

The King University School of Medicine is really in a bind. They desperately want their students to become surgeons, cardiologists, and pediatric neuroendocrinegastroenterologists. At the same time, they want to keep their accreditation, get some federal funding, and be considered cool by all those trendy state schools that turn out 180 "gatekeepers" a year to work at Upper Cheesefoot Peninsula County General Hospital. King Med's administrators thought they had found the perfect compromise when they allowed the Primary Care department to create a clinical medicine class for the MS-Is.

After all, the neonatal pulmonoradiologists figured, the primary care folks can't do too much damage in only three hours a week. But they didn't plan on the Primary Care department producing such a diabolical machine of forced caring and sensitivity to the patient's every need. They didn't plan on a mock-interview setting filled with time-outs and sniveling "patients" who threatened spontaneous weeping should an interviewer even consider being so insensitive as to explain their clinical situation without the use of hand puppets. They didn't plan, of course, on Clinical Arts.

I could spend hours discussing why Clinical Arts was a colossal waste of time, but in the past that discussion landed me in a meeting with the Dean to discuss my "attitude problem." So instead, let me use my first day on the wards to demonstrate how well Clinical Arts prepared me for the real practice of medicine.

I was on neurology and, armed with seventeen pieces of paper for note-taking and the knowledge gained during countless hours spent watching my fellow students interview actors, I was ready to admit my first patient. After ten minutes of getting-to-know-you questions guaranteed to put this bedridden stroke patient at ease, I began to delicately piece together her reasons, both conscious and subconscious, for coming to the hospital on this particular day. "So why did you decide to come here today?" I asked pleasantly. My patient's eyes narrowed, and she reassessed the 'health professional' sitting before her. "I had a stroke," Mrs. Daniels said, a little too matter-of-factly for my satisfaction. Obviously she was hiding something. Clinical Arts had taught me that you could only get the truth from a patient by dragging it out of her.

I allowed a big, friendly smile to spread over my face as I gently laid my hand on her knee (patients like to be touched). "Mrs. Daniels," I said warmly, "why did you really come here today?" This time she just stared at me icily. I could tell I was breaking down her defenses with the gentle yet firm manner I had been taught every patient needed. "You don't have to tell me," I cooed, making sure the patient still had her autonomy—the patient must never lose her autonomy—"but if you'd like to, I'm here to listen." I had played my ace early with that one, but I knew I had her. I had learned well the adversarial nature of the physician–patient relationship, actually a game of manipulation in which it was my duty to trick my opponent into telling me a truth she desperately wanted to hide.

I waited patiently, knowing that downtime was good for a patient, giving her time to think things over and come to grips with her situation. A few minutes passed. Mrs. Daniels looked expectantly at me and I looked right back at her, since eye contact is essential to making a patient feel comfortable enough to reveal her deep secret. Finally she opened her mouth to speak. "When can I see a doctor?" she asked coolly. The color ran out of my face and I got a sinking feeling in my stomach. I was losing control of the interview. The patient was winning the contest! I tried to calm myself so I could think clearly. Hug her? No, too early for that one. Cry, hoping to form a shared emotional bond? No, I had to think harder. Finally I hit upon the perfect counter: an open-ended question. I'd been taught that they work. Every single time.

For the next ninety minutes, I listened to Mrs. Daniels talk about her children, her flower garden, her magazine subscriptions, and her trip to Tennessee in 1952. I sat there furiously taking notes, knowing that the answer had to be hidden somewhere. During her story of learning to play the oboe in fourth grade, my resident entered the room. "So Mrs. Daniels, we looked at the films from the clinic and you did indeed have a stroke. We'll start you on some blood-thinners and you should be home in about four days. See you in the morning!"

Films? Clinic?! Blood-thinners?!? My resident must have gotten it wrong. She was only dealing with surface issues and had missed the root of the problem. Or had she? I listened for ten minutes more as Mrs. Daniels discussed how back in her day they used every part of the squirrel, and then excused myself and left. What had gone wrong? Had I missed doing one of my "learning issues" along the way? I was taught time and time again never to look at the chart, never to know the first thing about a patient before talking to her. I felt more disillusioned than the day I learned neither Milli nor Vanilli had sung their own songs.

Looking back, I realize that there had been no reason to talk to that patient at all. I could have spent eighteen seconds watching her draw a screwed-up clock face, listened to the radiology report over the phone, and made the diagnosis. I mean, if I wanted to sit around all day and listen to patients whine about stuff that's irrelevant and boring, I'd become a psychiatrist. A hospital is a place where people come to get better from their medical problems. If letting them talk for two hours about why Dale Earnhart is the best NASCAR driver despite being only fourth in the standings actually makes them better, then we shouldn't have to take physiology during the first year. But we do, and soon we'll also have to take a new course called "Practice," which is just Clinical Arts in disguise. Will it improve on Clinical Arts? It certainly can't be worse. Will the Primary Care department turn it into the same nauseating feel-a-thon it's replacing? I'm sure they will. Will we keep our accreditation? Of course—any school that turns out students who are forced to act as sensitively as we are will be showered with money by the government. Does it make your stomach churn as you realize what a bad sign that is for the future of our nation's health care system? It should.

I've been thinking about submitting this poem, based upon "Hop on Pop," to the *Annals of Surgery.*

Chop On Pop

We are surgeons.
We like to chop.
We just consulted
On your Pop.

He's feeling dizzy.
He's got some gout.
We feel we must
Take something out.

'Cause he's got an earache
And a pressure drop,
Only through surgery
Will these symptoms stop.

Medical management should be
Our first line, you say?
Do you want your father
To die today?

No, we must start cutting!
Start at the top!
We'll remove some organs!
We'll remove some glop!

Gallbladder, vagus,
Liver biopsy too.
We can try a Whipple.
(Those are hard to do!)

Sure it'll be messy
As we tear and lop.
He might bleed so much
We could need a mop!

But this is good for him,
It's the cut that heals.
Then we can drop some tubes
So he can get his meals.

And if he still feels bad
Or gets a systolic plop,
If vesicles arise
On an erythematous crop,

Then bring him back in!
We rise before the sun.
We have no outside lives,
We do this for fun.

Yes, we are surgeons.
We like to chop.
We cannot wait to get
Our hands on your Pop.

In The Garden Of Eden

Greetings from Eden. Some say it's paradise, but from the basement of Mrs. Tanner's house, it just looks like the place I'm doing my family medicine rotation. Practicing medicine in a tiny rural town takes some getting used to. In King Med's big city, you don't recognize the woman at the Food Lion by her ganglionic cyst. You don't look at the man in the car next to yours and wonder whether the hydrochlorothiazide got his diastolic pressure down below 110. But in Eden you do, and it's a bit weird.

But I'm not going to write about the oddities of Eden; that would fill volumes. Instead, I want to talk about my newest hobby—self-medication. Contrary to what one might think, the family doctor's office doesn't just contain stethoscopes and snot. It also holds boxes and boxes of medication left sitting on the counters by drug reps. For free! It's a big buffet of health and, as many people know, I am powerless to turn down anything that is free.

It started innocently enough. I have very thin membranes, so it only took me about fourteen minutes to get sick on my first day at the office: I opened my mouth to speak, and six little kids sneezed in it. By 8:30 A.M., my nose was like a faucet, and I began to search desperately for a way to turn it off. Just as I prepared to cauterize my nostrils, I noticed a green and yellow gleam coming from a closet. I whirled to face it and found myself staring into a sea of colors and slogans. And directly in the center sat a green box adorned with big yellow letters: Bromfed®. I'd never heard of it but, upon further investigation, I found that it contains psuedoephedrine. I thought I remembered that as an ingredient in SELDANE-D® , which worked well for my allergies, so I took one and my runny nose immediately slowed to a trickle. Pleased, I took another one an hour later, turning my nose into an arid desert of olfaction. I smiled.

I could have stopped there, but, as the day wore on, I again felt the lure of the drug closet. Peering in at the lovely reds, blues, and purples, I gained courage. I searched my body for some imperfection that could be cured with drugs, settling on the pinched nerve in my leg which, I hypothesized, could be due to inflammation. So I turned to the ibuprofen-laden shelves and decided to try the extra-strength MOTRIN® caplets. Unsatisfied with their taste, however, I sampled the orange-flavored chewable kind and have since made it my standard dessert, often on top of ice cream.

By this time, the Bromfed pills had made me sleepy. Some searching turned up a CLARITIN® tablet that promised to relieve my nasal congestion while not making me drowsy. I took a couple of pills, stuffed seven or eight into my pocket to get me through the night, and went home.

After a restful night of pink antibiotic dreams, I took one CLARITIN tablet and headed off to work. I fearlessly grabbed an Otis Spunkmeyer Wild-Blueberry-Super-Almond-Delight muffin in the office, ate every last oily crumb, and then calmly downed two MEVACOR® pills and one Lopid® tablet. Three hours later, I went to the bathroom and, just to make sure I didn't have a UTI, took a couple doses of cephalosporin. I was beginning to enjoy this. I even took some estrogen just for the heck of it. Yes, this hobby was exactly the kind of healthy diversion I needed to take my mind off the intense pressure of seeing earache after earache for nine hours straight.

A few days later, it occurred to me that maybe I should be concerned about drug interactions. It seemed unlikely, and besides, I figured the directions on the box would indicate if I was in danger. After all, who has time to read the tiny print in the little instruction inserts? All the same, I figured it couldn't hurt to take a couple antiarrhythmics prophylactically, just in case. I haven't looked back.

Yes, having a hobby has really invigorated me. There's always a reward at the end of each challenge-filled day, making the hard work not only less painful but also more satisfying. And this satisfaction with myself and in my work takes my mind off the misery of managing hypertensives who refuse to stop smoking. It's a good feeling, one I'd like to keep. Which is why, if I ever find myself losing interest in my hobby, I won't worry—I can always take a couple of free samples of Prozac® capsules.

But I Play One On TV

He arrived by helicopter in a driving rain and the crash cart team unloaded and wheeled him through the fog into the emergency room. An IV already dripping, he was rushed into Room 1 where, on the count of three, he was lifted onto the bed. "Car crash!" I heard somebody yell as a unit of plasma was hung. Doctors, nurses, and technicians raced in and out of the room, some shouting orders and others following them. I could feel the muscles of my neck begin to tense as I watched the flurry of activity. I felt as if I should help, but knew immediately that I couldn't. I felt the pressure in the room; the line that separated life and death hung low in the air, threatening at any moment to cross over the body of the patient who now lay untouched as the paddles, charged to 300, were placed on his chest. After an unsuccessful attempt, they were recharged and reapplied, this time answered by a beat. There was a sweaty sense of relief, and my own heartbeat slowed down. The patient was safe, at least for now.

I turned off the television in the sixth-floor lounge, relieved that everything at County General was once again under control and marveling at what a fine doctor Carter would become. I took the elevator down, navigated through the maze of white corridors, and reentered the King Med ER, where I was on pediatrics call. Sure enough, the kid with the otitis media "emergency" that I had seen two hours ago was still in Room 21, asleep and waiting for discharge. As I popped a CLARITIN tablet into my mouth and sat down to wait for something, preferably non-renal, to happen, my resident rushed over.

"Hey Jeff," he said in a voice I imagined was almost breathless. Just as it had upstairs, my pulse quickened. "I've got a kid in 18. I need you to get over there." I was already on my feet and grabbing for my bag, ready for action. "To watch him to see whether he vomits," he finished. I put my bag down. "Give him an hour. If nothing comes out, you can send him home." I sulked over to Room 18, chose a chair a good fifteen feet from the kid, and sat down to begin my vigil. I stared at the kid. He stared back. I wondered what Carter would do, but realized that he'd be too busy doing radical stomach resections to be in such a bland situation in the first place. My mind began to wander.

Based upon my dislike of drool and, actually, of fluids in general, I'd never expected to enjoy pediatrics. I figured I would put in my time, get my rotavirus, and be done with it. But as I watched the kid in front of me turn a slightly darker shade of green, I reflected that it hadn't been all bad. There were those happy-go-lucky clinic days spent defeating kids with congenital heart defects in *Ms. PacMan®*. There was the Halloween Fair where, even though I was told in no uncertain terms that I could not dress up as a worm load, I did load up with enough plastic spiders for a week. And I thoroughly enjoyed the Dermatology Clinic, although I found out later on that the "D" on my schedule actually stood for Diabetic Clinic—where I should have been. I smiled and was answered from fifteen feet away with a grimace of nausea and dismay. With these happy memories fresh in my head, though, I didn't even mind.

Sure, I thought, Carter and Dr. Ross have a basketball hoop in the alley behind the hospital. But I play ball in the East Campus gym every Sunday morning with all the peds residents. And when I'm on call until midnight, I get three, maybe four, free dinners in the cafeteria, some of them involving actual food. Maybe real life, I thought, is better than television after all. Maybe having real experiences is more valuable than living vicariously through people who are paid to pretend to have them. And maybe the satisfaction one can derive from accomplishing or failing at something far outweighs passively watching someone else do it. I looked back at my patient, yellowish drool running down the side of his pale, sunken cheek. Twenty-five more minutes to go. I hoped I had remembered to set my VCR to tape *Friends*.

Sew Close, Yet Sew Far Away

Finally I'm on surgery. All year you hear the stories: the sleep deprivation, the yelling, the student abuse, getting paged at 5:30 A.M. if you sleep through your alarm. But then you also hear about how cool it is to be in the OR and about the neat stuff you learn. You even hear that it can be fun. But no matter how many stories you hear, every med student must eventually find out what it's like for himself. Whether he wants to or not.

It's my third week of the rotation. As I entered this morning's carotid endarterectomy, I remembered my feelings of ambivalence on the first day of surgery. I realized that those feelings have completely disappeared, replaced, unfortunately, by new ones that are no easier to sort out. I grabbed the retractor and my eyes glazed over as I was hypnotized by the sound of suction. I began to think: Although I enjoy surgery more than anything else I've done in medical school, sadly, it still may not be the best career for me.

To begin with, it would be very tough to meet my future wife. I'm told that surgeons get the babes—heck, they do on television, and television never lies—but when do they meet them? I'm either in the hospital or asleep, and often both. Unfortunately, I'm not meeting any girls when I'm asleep, so the only place left is the hospital. Of course, there are some good-looking nurses. Just the other day, I assisted at a surgery staffed by a young, very attractive nurse. Unfortunately, the mask hides my cute medical-student-next-door smile and my protective goggles make me look like Kareem-Abdul Jabbar, although shorter and less Muslim. But I knew that saying just the right thing would overcome such obstacles. When I backed into the OR, she smiled and unfolded a gown for me. I placed my arms gently yet firmly in the sleeves and was about to suavely introduce myself when she spoke: "You're not sterile." My mouth hung open apishly as I tried to process this information.

"Your gown touched the monitor. Out." She whirled me around, pushed me toward the door and, before I could form a sentence with both a noun and a verb, I was out. I felt humiliated and, well, unclean.

The funny thing is, no one even knows I'm in the OR until the instant I adjust my mask or scrape the wax out of my ear, at which point sirens go off, sprinklers come on, and seven people "escort" me out of the room. But, as I stood outside the OR, scrubbing the subdermal layers from my arms, I began to think that maybe it was for the best. After all, the only conversation I know how to make these days is "Have you had any bowel movements in the last twenty-four hours?" And using this as a pickup line would probably lead to the use of more mace than I'm prepared for.

Another reason a career in surgery concerns me is that I'm not carrying much medical information around in my brain, or anywhere else for that matter. I was reminded of this when I was ripped out of my trance by the attending, who pointed at something—the neck I think—and asked, "What is it?"

"Uh, the carotid?" It was, after all, a carotid endarterectomy. I'm not stupid.

"Okay, wrong question," he continued. "Which nerve is it?"

"Er, the phrenic?" I was answered by a loud sigh.

"Okay, Jeffrey, this *vagus* nerve is lying on what muscle?"

"The sternocleidomastoid?" Another sigh. And so on.

Another thing that scares me is the new Autovalet system. At first, I was excited—no more trekking from the parking garage on those hot, sweaty days. I'd just pull up to the hospital and a nice young man in a red sports coat would park my car, whether I tipped him or not. I found it odd, however, that the same letter told me to report my scrub size. Days later, when the enormous vending monoliths were installed throughout the hospital, a cold chill seized my body as I realized what an Autovalet system was: an automated anti-theft scrubs-dispensing machine. Just as in George Orwell's "fictional" *1984*, I must now get my surgical attire from a machine designed by an evil mastermind to consistently, time after frustrating time, dispense scrubs two sizes too small.

So, these are the issues that will play a part in what may be the most important decision of my life. As much fun as surgery is, there are other things in life that, I've been told, are fun as well. And the decision rests, in the end, on how much I want to try them. To my sleep-deprived mind, as enjoyable as an entire decade of people screaming at me to "snip the sutures closer to the knot" sounds, I may, in the end, just not be cut out for it. No pun intended.

Here is my version of "How the Grinch Stole Christmas," which I'm thinking of submitting to the *American Journal of Clinical Pathology.*

How The Grinch Stole Christmas Factor

Now gather around
And I'll tell you a tale
About a Clotting Cascade
And how it can fail.

Yes, this is the story
Of the King-ites in Kingville.
And I know I must tell it
For if I don't, who will?

Ah, the King-ites were happy.
Their livers worked well,
With clotting factors produced
By each hepatic cell.

But up on a Hill
(Just down Tobacco Road),
Lived a thing called The Grinch,
With jealous rage he glowed.

"Just look at those King-ites,"
He growled with a sneer.
"So smug 'cause their med center
Is better than ours here.

"They think they can treat
Every single disease.
Well, I'll give them one
That'll bring them to their knees!

So that night as each King-ite
Dreamed sweet dreams in his head,
The Grinch put a contraption
In his pickup truck's bed.

There was a tungsten filament
On this crazy machine,
Which when hit by electrons
Emitted a beam.

"Now," laughed the Grinch,
"I can irradiate like the sun
I'll sneak into town
And ionize everyone!"

So he crept into Kingville,
Inside every home,
And mutated each male
King-ite's X chromosome.

The next morning when each
Got done shaving his face,
Each noticed their nicks
Bled all over the place.

This is odd, they all thought,
Our faces are oozy.
Our skin is all pale
And we're getting quite woozy.

They all went to the ED
And banged on the door.
So the triage nurse sent them
Up to the ninth floor.

"What is this?" the bleary-eyed
Heme-Onc intern said,
"You each need transfusions.
You each need a bed."

Then at once he decided,
"Hey, I should run a test."
But there was no attending
To say which was the best.

So he did a Chem-7
And a quick CBC,
Next a GI panel,
Then a tough ABG.

An ACTH,
T4, and T3,
Ketoconizole levels,
IgM, and IgG.

Finally, tired and lost,
He called for a fix.
The attending tried
A PTT with mix.

"They making thrombin," she said,
"And prekallikrein,
As well as vitamin K.
But what of Factor IX?"

"Oh," said the intern,
His confidence wrecked.
"It's hemophilia B
That you now suspect."

"It's true, my young 'tern,
This is what I've suspected.
Though usually only one in
One hundred thousand's affected."

"Well, no matter," she said,
Turning to the ill men,
"I have good news to tell—
You will soon clot again!

"You'll all now be getting
The fresh-frozen plasma you crave.
You'll be going home soon—
Your Christmas Factor is saved!"

The sick men all cheered
At this turn in direction.
Not a single one minded
The high risk of viral infection.

Meanwhile, back on the Hill,
The Grinch gave a long sigh.
(And if you looked closely,
You'd see a tear in his eye.)

"Now I know why these King-ites
All feel that they're blessed.
For indeed, their med center
Is by far the best."

The VA Spa

Surgery at King Med was becoming too easy. I needed to examine more necrotic feet. I needed to devote three pages to the surgical history alone. Yes, what I needed was to rotate through the Veterans Administration Hospital (affectionately known as the 'VA'). So, I started myself on a slow, continuous drip of vancomycin and headed across the street for the most dreaded part of the surgery clerkship. Sure, I still roam the halls of King Med now and then, frantically searching for the room housing this week's Chairman's Conference, where someone usually comments helpfully that the VA is really great because "you get to do a lot of stuff there."

What nobody seems to understand, though, is that I don't *want* to do lots of stuff. I want to tell my resident that I'm going to see a surgery on the other side of the sterile core and then go watch talk shows in the student lounge, booing and hissing with the rest of America at the mothers who steal their daughters' boyfriends. I want to "go see my patients," and end up in the sub-basement of the orange zone playing *Ms. PacMan* with the cystic fibrosis kids. I'm not interested in listening to more rhonchi. I don't want to change another moist, green dressing. I want to stand for a couple minutes while my intern talks, nod my head a lot, and then go eat bagels and do crossword puzzles where no one can see me.

"You can be totally responsible for your patients," they often continue enthusiastically. But I enjoy being *partially* responsible for my patients or, more precisely, reporting their lab results to somebody else and letting him worry about it. Total responsibility means taking H&Ps, which is impossible at the VA because *(a)* I understand very few of the words that come out of my patients' mouths and *(b)* the charts are little more than a random stack of papers that may or may not pertain to the patient in question.

So, when I get a new patient to work up, I go say a fast hello, catch some weird strain of MRSA, rifle through his file, and then write him up as a patient presenting with a hernia. And I'm never wrong. Because what most people don't realize is that to be admitted to the VA, you must not only be a member of the armed services but also have some bowel hanging into some place it shouldn't be (often the mythical region known as "inguinal"). Some days, there is actually a line of veterans outside the hospital coughing and valsalva-ing like crazy, trying to get some sort of reducible mass to show.

Eventually, all these hernia patients that I am totally responsible for end up in the VA's operating room where I, in a totally responsible manner, stand with my face mashed into the side of somebody's shoulder and hold a retractor. The ORs at the VA are much smaller and homier than those at King Med, more like bathrooms with a huge anesthesia machine. They are so homey, in fact, I often feel I can touch whatever I like. But each day the scrub nurse reminds me this is not the case by joyfully announcing that the medical student has once again contaminated himself, in the gleeful tone of a young girl who has just found a bag of jellybeans. So I re-scrub in the city water, reminding myself that at least I'm not out on the floor trying to draw blood.

Drawing blood at the VA is like trying to fit a garden hose into a one-cell-thick straw that is rolling around beneath a big shag rug. Usually I end up just taking my own blood and scraping the needle on the curtain before squirting it into the test tube, since it doesn't really matter which methicillin-resistant bug the lab finds anyway.

But after spending two and a half weeks getting used to the overwhelming smell and to not having any tourniquets, I think I'm going to be okay. All the fluid I ever wanted is right here for the draining. And though they were a bit wary of me at first, the patients, some of whom have been in the same bed since before the use of ether, are beginning to accept me. After all, just riding the elevators has given me a seven pack-year smoking history.

Furthermore, I'm getting used to this idea of having "total responsibility" for my patients. Certainly, once I become an actual doctor, I'll be the sole physician for most of the people under my care. So I guess the VA setting, where I have a whole team of residents and attendings to back me up, is the best place to learn how to take total control of a patient's illness and everything involved with trying to cure it. Nevertheless, each night at 11:30 P.M., as I change my thirteenth moist, green dressing of the day, I can't help but think I'd still rather be playing *Ms. PacMan*.

The Great Bacteria Myth

I recently discovered that I'm not allergic to sulfa drugs after all. I hadn't taken any in the fifteen years since I learned of my drug "allergy." None, that is, until the other night when, while I was on call for OB/GYN, my toothache of gestational age six weeks, realizing it had reached every pain nerve in my mouth and some in my arm, actually began creating new ones. I felt like a half-crazed junkie as I dragged my body to the pharmacy at four in the morning. Of course, most half-crazed junkies probably don't beg for broad-spectrum antibiotics, but I was desperate. When the sympathetic pharmacist broke the law and gave me a few SEPTRA®, I happily swallowed them, even as a little voice in the back of my head (the "occiput") warned me that this could mean more IgE activity than the time my friend's cat fell asleep on my eyeballs.

By the time I finally understood what I had ingested, however, the pills were past the skeletal muscle and there was nothing I could do but sit in the oddly fishy smelling call room and wait for my skin to fall off. But, as the sun rose to what I imagined was the sound of millions of bacteria screaming as their Golgi complexes were extruded into the extracellular space, I found I was still intact. No anaphylaxis. No hives. Just me and a lot of busy macrophages. And that was when I knew for certain what I had long suspected: there is no such thing as bacteria.

You're thinking this is as baseless as some of my other theories, such as that the renal system can't be learned and that pediatrics residents never actually went to medical school. Well, I'm prepared to prove this so convincingly that you won't have to read my upcoming article in *The New England Journal of Medicine*. So don't even look for it.

To begin with, I've done about three months of surgery and have contaminated myself, they tell me, each and every day. I calculate there are approximately 210 patients who were exposed to my flora, a couple of whom I know did not become infected. I haven't bothered with any "statistics" or "analyses," but if you graphed this sample against the incidence of infection, would you get a parabola or a straight line or . . . something? I hardly think so.

Another relevant personal experience is that I take a shower every morning in a tub that my landlord's lawyer tells me used to be white. So there I am, warm and moist with all my membranes exposed, surrounded by a brown film, and I only get sick about once a month, not every day. As an experiment, I scrubbed one side of the tub with detergent and after a while some film came off. What happened when I dropped a 1500 mg tablet (three times the recommended dose!) of amoxicillin on the other side? Nothing!

I'm sure you're thinking, "O.K., I'm convinced, but what happens when the drug companies find out about this?" I'm going to let you in on a secret, one that could force me to hide in a cabin in Montana within forty-eight hours of publication: the drug companies already know. But they want the world to become so terrified of disease that people will buy even more high-priced drugs to combat "drug resistant" bacterial strains. What a scam! The reason rifampin costs so much isn't just because it turns everything that cool reddish color. The drug companies spend billions of dollars each year to pay scientists to pretend they're constantly researching new antibacterial cures that begin with the letters "ceph." When was the last time you read an article questioning whether bacteria really exist? Not for over a hundred years. Think about it.

If you're like me, you believe what your senses tell you. Several ancient schools of Greek philosophy were based on this very idea, and even though they were only thinking about things like sandals and plazas, the paradigm applies to bacteria as well. Have *you* ever seen a bacterium? Perhaps your sixth-grade science teacher showed you a piece of dirt floating under the microscope and claimed it was one. But did you ever see a disaccharide capsule? Or flagella in a 9-2 arrangement? I bet you didn't, and neither did your teacher. Of course, back then, they also thought protozoa were plants, but that's neither here nor there. The point is, no one's ever heard, smelled, or touched a bacterium.

To those who remain skeptical, I offer one last scrap of evidence—my microbiology grade. Could anyone do so badly in a class based solely on fact and still become a physician? For the sake of humanity, let us hope not.

O.K., you're thinking, but how do you explain fevers, abscesses, and pus? I'll explain those clinical situations in just three syllables: Bad Humors. Without going into a lengthy discussion about the Aether and the intricacies of phrenology, I'll simply state that while medicine has made a lot of advances over the last century, it's a shame that all this antibiotic voodoo has wriggled its way into disease treatments. A simple regimen of trephining, bloodletting, and alternating hot and cold baths makes good sense, and it's cost-effective as well.

So there's my theory. I'm sure many of you are relieved, while others may still be confused, grasping for something ciliated to cling to. But bacteria are a myth, and the sooner we accept this, the sooner our patients will benefit.

Unfortunately, this doesn't interest my dentist who, despite my eloquent arguments and desperate groveling, continues to hang on to his antiquated beliefs. One root canal and $1200 later, I find it sad that not everyone is as progressive and informed as I am.

Cents And Sensibilities

After one year and nine months in medical school, after 45.6 fortnights of drudgery, after 639 days of tedium, after 15,336 hours of boredom, I have become medically inspired. It struck during the twenty-first hour of one of my on-call nights in labor and delivery. As I stared at the fetal heart tracing from my fully dilated patient, the late decelerations and poor variability peacefully illuminated by the rising sun, I saw my future so clearly that I almost forgot the amniotic fluid dripping down my arm. I was being called for a special purpose. And, powerless to ignore my destiny, I knew I should simply give myself to it without resistance. Willful choice was no longer an option: upon graduation, I would open my own birthing clinic.

At first, the call frightened me—how would I accomplish my mission? Where should I start? Would Medicare reimburse me? But, soothed by the soft irregularity of my patient's increasingly labored breathing, I decided that running my own birthing clinic could work out just fine. I just needed to fine-tune the procedures I was learning and my clinic would be spitting out record numbers of babies in no time. The ideas began to come even faster and louder than my patient's pleas for an epidural.

First, too much time and money is spent on women with false labor pains or incorrect claims of water breakage. In my clinic, anyone who steps through the door more than thirty-five weeks pregnant will be induced. Why wait around for the miracle of birth to start naturally when drugs can prevent an extra trip to the hospital for the patient and an additional admit note for me? In my opinion, there's no naturally selected, evolutionarily advantageous process that can't be improved by synthetic compounds that have been proven occasionally effective in rats. Besides, I think my slogan, "The sooner you get it out, the sooner you're not fat," will strike a chord in my patients, many of whom want to look good for the prom.

Another thing I realized, as I watched a head begin to emerge from what looked to me like a pretty uncomfortable place, is that you don't need an advanced degree and four years of training to deliver babies. All you need is one of those pregnancy wheels the drug companies hand out. That wheel and a 400-page manual on how to use it are enough to turn any junior-high graduate into an adequate baby deliverer. Those wheels give you more than dates and gestational ages—if used correctly they can, I believe, also suggest likely names and even determine paternity. Under dire circumstances, if left alone in the room with a "ripe" patient, I believe the wheel could do a successful forceps delivery and, perhaps, even begin breast-feeding.

Perhaps my most revolutionary idea, but the one that I believe history will one day most completely justify, hopefully to the satisfaction of the legal system, is this: Rather than waste time and effort constantly pleading with my patients to take their prenatal vitamins and folic acid, I will simply fortify beer with these essential nutrients. A large proportion of my patients are going to drink no matter what I say and, if my plan works, I may even try fortifying wine, cigarettes, and cocaine to give my patients a choice. A satisfied customer is more likely to bring her business back to my clinic for her next seven or eight pregnancies.

Now, many people know that I called a Hospital Unit Coordinator (HUC) a bad word—an alarmingly bad word—followed by the word "moron." This was, of course, only because it was true. To prevent unfortunate incidents such as this in my clinic, I'm simply not going to have any HUCs. True, the phone will probably get answered more, people will receive a greater proportion of their messages, charts will be put together in a more correct and timely fashion, and the average-weight-per-employee will drop by thirty-five pounds. Nevertheless, this is an experiment I'm willing to try, even though I'm sure some union or another will attempt to bring me to court, which will be unfortunate, since I'm not going to hire any lawyers either.

As I stood at the foot of my patient's bed, trying unsuccessfully to untangle the umbilical cord from the emerging neck, it seemed to me that, yes, a birthing clinic might just be the area of medicine where I could carve my niche. More than just a great way to meet single teenage girls, it would be a chance to hear each newborn's first cry, to watch each take his or her first breath. It would be an opportunity to watch the expression on each new mother's face change from pain to relief to joy as she catches her first glimpse of the child she has produced. It would be a chance to bring the joy of life to hundreds of young people with private insurance. And, of course, there would be no one to tell me I was contaminated.

Lost in thought, I smiled as the newborn baby swung back and forth by its umbilical cord, occasionally bumping gently into my knees. Heck, anybody can do this, I thought and, infused with excitement, I gently laid the neonate on the ground and ran off to fill out the birth report. I knew mine would be the best birthing clinic ever.

PTSD: Pediatrics Traumatic Stress Disorder

Even though my pediatrics rotation was so long ago I should only remember it in terrifying late-night flashbacks after eating Mexican food, the number-one thing people still say to me, after "What's that hanging off your chin?" is "Hey, I heard you really hated pediatrics." I don't deny it—I just prefer to bury the experience in a tight little ball of anger deep inside until, one day after my 374th pelvic exam of the afternoon, I snap and begin to Doppler nearby inanimate objects to "listen to their aura."

When asked why I hated pediatrics so much, I always feel obliged to answer. This usually turns into a twenty-minute harangue, leaving the wide-eyed questioner backing away slowly and trying not to make any sudden movements. Since my dislike of my pediatrics rotation has become so well known, I've decided to tell all as a sort of therapy session. Maybe then I'll be able to hear the word "fontanel" without starting to foam at the mouth. Maybe.

The reason for my hatred is pretty simple. If you were told to sit in a room for eleven hours a day and give two-minute descriptions of the same patients over and over again to different doctors who weren't even listening, you'd think you were in some sort of prison camp. However, I don't think the laws of international warfare allow anyone to make people sit through two hours of sign-out rounds listening to the residents scream at each other about whether to give a kid six or eight units of insulin.

At the beginning of the rotation, everyone is told that one of the medical student's main jobs is to play with the kids. The only way to do that, though, is to bring the kid to rounds. If they are present, however, the kids will want to start drawing vancomycin levels and prescribing IV antibiotics, which are the only duties that peds residents actually perform other than complaining. Even if I had been allowed to bring my patients to rounds, I wouldn't have been able to since I never actually saw them—seeing the kids wasn't encouraged. But since all little kids look the same (covered with drool) and are, in theory, interchangeable, if you give the wrong kid a dose of tobramycin it's okay. Chances are he needed it anyway.

But, I'm happy to report, there is a way to get through pediatrics. Just remember one simple idea: pediatrics is nothing more than internal medicine for little people. Kids are no different than adults—they're just smaller. Think about it. Every adult weighs seventy kilograms (apparently about 308 pounds), so they all get the same dose of a drug. But peds patients come in a variety of sizes, from little to littler. Learn a few easy-to-remember conversions and you immediately know the drug dosage for any patient in hectare-bushels per deciknot-pound.

Furthermore, kids get the same diseases as adults. When kids get them, however, the Kouncil of Idiotic Diseases and Stuff (K.I.D.S.) gives the illnesses cool names, like Ondine's Curse. Accurately diagnosing kids isn't all that important anyway, since every pediatric disease only really causes nausea and vomiting. If a patient has any other complaint, she is either a three-year-old malingerer looking to get free drugs or a midget.

That was my brief diatribe on pediatrics. Don't get me wrong—I don't dislike kids, although they are, technically speaking, merely little bags of drool. They have their purposes, I'm sure, and I don't even mind taking care of them as long as *(a)* they're asleep; *(b)* they don't get sick after 4:00 P.M.; and *(c)* I'm not in a room with six whining, screaming residents talking about them for seventeen hours a day. But for four weeks of my life I was, and I'll never get those four weeks back. Well, I'm not going to think about it anymore. It's time to go Doppler my couch.

In honor of "One Fish, Two Fish, Red Fish, Blue Fish" by Dr. Seuss, I've thought about sending this poem to the *American Journal of Ophthalmology.*

One Cone, Two Cone, Red Cone, Blue Cone

One cone,
Two cone,
Red cone,
Blue cone.

A superficial gray opacity's a corneal scar.
Myopic eyes can't see too far.
What a scary number of eye diseases there are!

Homonomous hemianopsia's the tragic fact
When you have a lesion in your optic tract,
And, though you may still accommodate and react,
No red reflex suggests a cataract.

Exophthalmos signals Graves' disease,
Torturous vessels are copper wire arteries,
Retinal reattachment holds no guarantees,
But success is increased in retinoic acid implantees.

For yellow sclera, jaundice is the cause,
Episcleritis produces nodular flaws,
Trigeminal lesions numb your face and jaws,
And for blepharitis, wipe with wet, warm gauze.

Most muscles are controlled by cranial nerve III,
But you need cranial nerve II so you can see.
Edinger-Westphal's purpose always escapes me,
But without the optic nerve you get atrophy.

An enlarged optic cup suggests glaucoma,
Either one or two hits gives retinoblastoma.
And you don't need some kind of fancy diploma
To know not to induce mydriasis if they're in a coma.

One cone,
Two cone,
Red cone,
Blue Cone.

Back To The Future

Dr. A. D. Minstrator,

Enclosed is my final project for your Cost-Effective Medicine course. I think it is both practical and effective. I hope you feel the same.

The Cost-Effective Use of Leeches to Treat Various Maladies

As the climate of medicine changes, it is becoming evident that costs must be contained in every way possible so patients can afford the care that they deserve. Because a bunch of lawyers and business people have decided that everyone has the right to demand health care and, consequently, the services of doctors and associated medical professionals simply by walking into the emergency department, health care costs have skyrocketed. Furthermore, since many consumers are unable to pay for their own health care (including biweekly ED detox sessions), these administrators have also decided that individuals who earn more money should pay for the care of those who earn less. Therefore, the current health care system cannot provide adequate care to those with actual medical illnesses and who need our superior technology and facilities.

This financial bind is relatively new in the health care community. Only recently have costs risen to such an extent that average taxpayers can no longer pay for their own health care, much less for the care of others who prefer to collect unemployment rather than get a job bagging groceries. In difficult situations, it is sometimes best to look to the past for answers. It should come as no surprise, then, that the solution presented here had been employed for centuries, only recently going out of vogue. As the title makes clear, the solution I propose is Leeches.

For hundreds of years, medical professionals have used the leech to drain the body of bad humors, red phlegm, and poisoned blood. Although efficacy rates from the fourteenth century are currently unavailable, this treatment was the preferred cure for many ailments and, therefore, must have done its job a fair amount of the time. Only recently has it fallen by the wayside, replaced by the current technology boom, which has given us electronic equipment and fancy

60

medicines to deal with illnesses previously treated by means only moderately less well-understood and with only somewhat worse outcomes.

Why bring leeches back? Why offer our patients, rich and poor alike, a less desirable, yet fairly treatment when we can do better? The answer is simple—cost. One bag of vancomycin for a resistant kidney infection costs hospitals about $200. Attaching five or six leeches to the patient's flank, with replacement every two hours by a P.A. or nurse leechist, would cost only pennies. A workup for fever of unknown origin, the internist's nightmare, would cost approximately three dollars for leeches instead of the current thousands of dollars in unrecovered funds. Obviously, a dramatic savings.

What are the clinical indications for the use of leeches in the twenty-first century? Many assume the need for hundreds of costly double-blind placebo trials comparing the use of actual leeches (experimental group), plastic leeches (placebo group), and other procedures known to be curative (control group). Happily, this cost can be avoided. After a good deal of research, the author has determined that, just as in the past, the leech could be used to cure many maladies from smallpox to dementia praecox. True, the exact number of leeches and length of administration are not immediately apparent. But those determinations can be left to epidemiologists and hospital administrators, many of whom have master's degrees in administration.

Am I proposing a perfect system? Of course not. But as problems arise, they will be dealt with in a cost-effective manner. For example, HIV transmission can be (mostly) avoided by performing random tests on the leeches between their use on different patients. Although it is too expensive to provide new leeches for each administration, this random testing should reveal approximately 94 percent of the leeches that are infected, and these can then be discarded (cost-effectively) in a nearby pond.

To supply this "new" treatment, a Leech Center would be created. The leeches would be bred, raised, stored, packaged, and eventually disposed of at this location. The estimated cost of installing the necessary equipment for such a facility, to be housed in the unneeded transfusion labs, is approximately $29,400. Staffing costs for the Center would be approximately $140,000 per year. Overhead would be negligible, since the leeches would not have to be fed and would breed among themselves. The net amount saved by the hospital from reducing the number of surgeries and radiologic procedures, decreasing the length of hospital stays, and decreasing the amount of antimicrobials used is estimated to be at least $317,640,000. This is money that can be passed along to all the patients' insurers and actuaries.

In conclusion, although this system would not provide the outstanding level of care currently available at King Med, given today's economic and political climate, it is by far the most logical solution to what many view as important questions about health care's economic crisis. Many naysayers will protest a return to such a crude and barbaric form of medicine in light of the fantastic technology brought to us over the past few decades. Granted, using leeches may not work as well as liver transplants and radiation oncology. But I say that in these times in which everybody wants to live forever in perfect health without paying for it, how can we afford not to?

Soap Box

As I close the book on my second year, it is time to dust off my mental ophthalmoscope and assess the fundus of my medical school experience. Adjusting my focus, I hope I will see reassuring creamy pinkness and sharp disc margins, and not the engorgement and swelling characteristic of the venous stasis of papilledema.

Unfortunately, a year of clinical medicine has ground me into another SOAP-note-writing zombie. I even write my grocery lists in SOAP format. Thinking back over my goals for the last fourteen months (learn how to deal with patients in an effective and professional manner; determine how not to get screwed by the OB/GYN department; etc.), I jotted down this note in the hope of making a healthy recovery.

Subjective: Patient is tired. Very, very tired. So tired, in fact, that when suddenly awakened by a slimy trail of drool creeping down his neck, he fell out of his chair during attending rounds. Complaints include increased confusion and feelings of entrapment; he may spend hours in a room doing nothing, and yet feels unable to leave. Patient also complains of large, indurated mass on back of leg that he believes became infected several days after he injected himself with IM Phenergan® to relieve nausea reportedly of an idiopathic nature.

Objective: Thin, pale, undernourished white male. Becomes sweaty and starts to fidget when forced to compile differential diagnoses of seven thousand items for lower back pain. Undergoes mental-status changes when forced to write the same order thirteen times before the HUC stops talking to her girlfriends on the phone and waiting for her nails to dry and starts to do her job. Speaks in neologisms and word-salads, especially when presenting a patient to attendings. Recently seroconverted to PPD-positive status secondary to being exposed to the VA hospital.

Assessment: Looking back at the past year, patient believes he has spent an inordinate amount of time doing nothing. Often this was disguised as holding retractors, measuring cervical dilation, and taking the pediatrics rotation. These experiences replaced many activities he enjoys more, including reading, playing basketball, sleeping, and talking to girls, although a retrospective study has shown that girls wouldn't have talked to him anyway.

However, as vigorously as he tried to resist, he did learn many things, some of which dealt with medicine. Began to understand basic medical principles, such as the pathophysiology of mitral stenosis and where the neck is located. Furthermore, began to function as a member of the medical team in some capacity, which made the entire exercise somewhat more worthwhile. Met a lot of residents he liked and made many good friends. Was able to spend time with his classmates, some of whom he already knew and others whom he got to know better, for which he was grateful. Was even able to have some fun at work. In the end, found himself enjoying the company of people with similar interests doing something he found increasingly gratifying.

Began to imagine that he too could become a fully operational physician and that the huge amount of necessary information was not out of reach, but only required time and experience to be mastered. Began to see himself as not only an instrument of healing but also a staff of knowledge and, even, a scepter of power. Began to imagine himself ruling over a community of vassals who both worshipped and feared him, carved graven images in his likeness, and prepared offerings of meat and dried fruits to leave on the altar of the cathedral erected in his honor.

Then he realized he had fallen asleep in attending rounds again and, wiping the drool from his neck, listened to somebody drone on about indications for catheterization for another forty-five minutes.

Plan: 1. Sleep until November.
2. Consider applying to law school in the spring.

BOOK THREE

My Life As A Lab Rat

Postcard From The Edges

Apart from my acceptance into medical school, I have experienced only two ACTS OF GOD in the last three years. Now, some might call all three events natural disasters, but I'm not that cynical. The two Acts of which I speak are the Blizzard of '96, which hit during the first weekend of my surgery rotation, and Hurricane Fran, which whirled through last weekend, the first weekend of my third year. And as this past windy weekend blew by me, I realized that the way I handled each Act reflected, in essence, the difference between the second year of medical school behind me and the third year still ahead. I will try to explain by contrasting each Act's key moments.

Alarm-less, I awoke this past Friday morning at noon, just after Hurricane Fran came through. I had no electricity and nothing to do for the entire day other than go for a walk and read a book. The Friday after the Blizzard of '96 descended, I woke up at 4:30 A.M. to find my car door frozen shut, necessitating an icy two-mile hike to the hospital, where I spent twelve hours retracting organs in surgery. That night I called everyone I knew to try to get a ride home, but I ended up walking again beneath the soft pink sky that heralded only the coming of more snow. On this last Friday night, though, I called up my friend Keith. Twenty minutes later, relaxing in his ancient Porsche convertible beneath the glow of a million stars, we were headed toward the state line and leaving the hurricane-damaged region far behind. By 1 A.M. we rolled into a small college town and, despite not knowing a soul, by 4:30 we were peacefully asleep on the couch belonging to some girls we'd just met. At that same hour during the Blizzard of '96 weekend, I was putting on my earmuffs in preparation for another frozen trudge to the hospital.

After waking at noon this last Saturday, Keith and I headed to Washington, D.C., as the afternoon sun tanned our well-rested skin. Cute females waved from their cars and tried to get us to chase them, but Keith's Porsche is an "English gentleman's car," which means it can't go over 68 mph. We arrived at 2 P.M. and gave ourselves a tour of the city before dropping by a friend of Keith's to wash up. In contrast, during that wintry Saturday afternoon on call in the OR, I was given a tour of the chest cavity, which I would actually have seen if my resident had had a transparent neck, which he didn't. Eventually, I contaminated myself and was sent outside to scrub again. I returned to the derisive scowls and mocking laughter of the OR nurses; no one offered me a sterile towel so I could dry my hands.

Last weekend, though, as I dropped some feta cheese into my lap while attending a bon voyage party with Keith and his friend, my error was met only with friendly laughter and several offers to help me clean myself up. And while everyone at the party spoke French, they were considerate of my ignorance and happily translated everything into English for my benefit. In contrast, the surgeons in the OR spoke in terms strange to a new student on surgery. Words that sounded like "sonometer," "bovey," and "femur" left me feeling confused and, well, ignorant.

When surgery ended, I was free to eat the remains of some burnt macaroni and cheese before heading back to the floor to draw blood and check the patients' stools for blood so that I could see if I needed to draw even more blood. Last weekend in D.C., however, I had dinner at Capezio's, where my cousin and I spent a long evening catching up before he picked up the check. I didn't monitor a single bowel movement the entire night.

Then we were off to Georgetown, where we ended the evening leaning against a balcony and sipping margaritas as the city passed by below. On the Saturday night during the Blizzard, I remember gazing out of my patient's hospital room window at the happy passersby below, each of whom had a life that didn't involve waiting for Mrs. Freeman to finish her bowel movement so they could check her stool for blood. But it wasn't long before I was back in the call room, fast asleep and drooling the satisfied drool of the med student who didn't have to draw any more blood for three hours.

Sunday morning last weekend, Keith and I woke up refreshed. We met one of my college buddies for lunch, took a quick look at the National Gallery of Art, and then spent a scenic four hours chasing the setting sun back home. That Sunday on surgery, I was up at 6 A.M., and finished with my work by noon. After a fifteen-minute break to look at a three-month-old issue of *Sports Illustrated,* I spent the rest of the day in the library working on my hernia paper, the fluorescent lights reflecting off my pale, sickly skin. As nine o'clock rolled around on both nights, I was drifting off to sleep in my bed. After my D.C. visit, I had happy memories of an adventure just finished; after my surgery call, dim recollections of a weekend that existed for nearly everyone in the world but me.

And there, in stark contrast, are the two Acts, each a microcosm of an entire year. However, they don't tell the *whole* story. I actually liked my surgery rotation, the residents, and what they taught me. In fact, of all the rotations I did last year, I enjoyed surgery the most. At times, the prospect of doing surgery for my entire life thrilled me. But that's easy to say now, after working in the lab just six hours a day for two weeks. When I think back to that cold Sunday night, I can still hear the wind churn against my window as I fought back sleep to write in permanent black ink across my shoulder, "Don't ever become a surgeon." I read it every day as I got into my scrubs.

Last Sunday night, as I lay in total blackness, I wrote a short note on the pad next to my bed: "Don't forget to turn the power back on." Worn down from my second year of medical school, I find I'm still trying very hard to do just that.

I really think that *Progress in Cardiovascular Diseases* will snap this poem up. My thanks to Dr. Seuss for writing "Horton Hears A Who."

Morton Hears A Murmur

There once was a doctor
Named Morton, you see,
Who wanted to practice
Cardiology.

So he listened to tapes
And used Harvey with verve.
He even studied
The Frank-Starling curve.

And then he soon felt
He was ready to start,
So he went to the wards
In search of a heart.

(But sadly for Morton,
He was at the VA,
So not one normal heart
Would he hear that day.)

He found his first patient,
Who was not looking well,
Put his stethoscope on,
Used the diaphragm, then the bell.

He listened quite hard.
He listened quite long.
And he knew that something
Was very, very wrong.

But he didn't know what,
Much less what to do;
He just knew he heard more
Than S1 and S2.

He heard a rumbling sound
At the right sternal border.
But which valve did that mean?
He never could keep them in order!

Did it crescendo? Radiate?
Did it sound pansystolic?
Did it matter that his patient
Was an eighty pack-year alcoholic?

Was it mitral? Tricuspid?
Or pulmonary?
Did it sound like stenosis
Or insufficiency?

He checked the carotids
For bruits and thrills,
Palpated the thyroid,
And asked about chills.

Then he measured the amplitude
With those Popsicle sticks.
They didn't move, so he thought,
"Ah, a I out of VI!"

Morton had him Valsalva,
Then squat and then stand.
Then he palpated the femoral
For pulsus alternans.

But he found nothing at all,
To Dr. Morton's dismay.
So tired, defeated,
He had just one thing to say:

"I feel so worthless here
Make this all go away!
Oh, nurse, take him to echo,
I'm done for the day."

True Lies

Like *Pseudomonas* into a new wound, the time has come once again for an eager horde of gram-negative medical students to form a fresh abscess in the amphitheater of King Med. This abscess cannot be drained by mere aspiration under fluoroscopic guidance. No, it will take eleven months of mind-numbing boredom before this colony has its virility sucked out of it. Sure, there will be some resistant strains at first. But these will slowly be overcome by more sheer monotony than the creators of penicillin ever thought possible.

What should an MS-I do? Substitute different glycoproteins into your capsules? Transfer into law school? Fortunately, I have prepared a short outline of things to watch out for. By following my instructions to the letter, you will not only have a better first-year experience, but also allow me to insidiously gain control of your thoughts and actions. I used to tell my friends that I could hold their hands only so long before they'd have to go out into the world and do things on their own. Today they all make $55,000 a year for carrying a briefcase and playing on the Internet for thirty-six hours a week, while I'm preparing to spend a year looking at pulmonary nodules and only have to pay $22,500. So, as you can see, it really is in your best interest to follow my advice.

Therefore, I now present my safe but effective method for becoming the happiest and most successful medical student you can be, without taking steroids.

Don't try to learn the renal system. Nobody understands it, including the instructors who attempt to teach it to you. They'll talk about "nephrons" and "glomeruli" and more tubes and pumps than are in the New York City subway system (although the subway actually contains more urine). But don't be fooled by their fancy terms and diagrams—studies now show that the renal system may not even exist. My own theory is that the kidneys are simply vestigial stomachs left over from our bovine ancestors. I'll bet my future income ($64.51 per year) that our colleagues in anthropology will soon prove me right, though nothing that is printed here can be considered legally binding in a court of law.

Don't go near the Family Medicine department. They'll smile and offer you barbecues and ice cream socials. All you have to do is join the Family Medicine interest group, which meets monthly in the forest to talk about their feelings and to be sensitive to each other's emotional needs. But once they have their claws in you, it's nearly impossible to wrest free. Soon you'll be in the "rural health coalition," driving two hours to East Toenail Peninsula Township to hand out pamphlets filled with big pictures illustrating the advantages of brushing one's teeth after eating house paint. Then it's only a matter of time before you start attending the mind-body study group's Friday afternoon lectures (healing crystals are not provided). Before you know it, you'll be a family practitioner in Upper Little Mudclump Falls County, where you'll grow your own digoxin and have to perform fundal exams with a candle until the general store can have a new battery for your flashlight carried in on the next mule train.

Don't forget that there's a fifty-fifty chance you're smarter than your big sib. Sure, he's going to give you lots of advice, but the fact that he's already gone through gross anatomy and you haven't doesn't mean a thing. Go ahead and bring that bone box home. After all, you've got his test file and you know darn well that he once thought the testicular artery sent collaterals to the uterus. Which brings up something else of note:

Your test file. Don't spend time reading books with silly names like *Biochemistry* and *Anatomy*. Don't waste time going to lectures. For that matter, never leave your living room. Instead, the night before an exam, look at the tests from the previous seventy-eight years (some written on parchment or slate) and you'll learn all you need to pass the test. Mind you, I'm not saying you'll know everything relevant to the subject of the pentose shunt. But, since many questions haven't been changed in decades, learning about recent advances in clinical medicine, starting with the advent of, say, forceps, is pointless. So, memorize how to trephine a skull. Learn how to control a polio epidemic. Your future patients won't thank you, but at least you'll pass the test and land a great position in academics.

Don't trust the OB/GYN department. The residents are great and you can learn a lot. But the department will say that the written final doesn't play a big part in your grade. Which is a lie. And there's nothing you can do about it. Not that I'm bitter.

I could go on and on, though I'm sure it seems as if I already have. Some of you may be thinking that perhaps it's best to make your own mistakes. This is a reasonable point of view, chosen by many when faced with my advice, and no one will fault you for doing so. Follow your heart and do what feels right. And, of course, if you do decide to ignore me and do things the hard way, don't worry: there are plenty of pulmonary nodules to go around.

Life As A Lab Rat

Originally, I had planned to go to graduate school to get a Ph.D. in psychology. But after I realized that my reply to most patients would be "just suck it up and deal," I set my sights on a more satisfying career (not that that wouldn't have been satisfying). Thwarted in my attempt to become a space archeologist, after several minutes of hard thought, I decided to check out medical school. And, except for the nights before tests and every day on the wards, I've never regretted my decision. Now that I'm in the lab, however, I've gotten a peek at what life is like in Ph.D.-land.

After spending a couple of months in the lab, it would be unfair of me to withhold any longer my observations about how this life differs from that on the wards. As soon as I embarked on this train of thought, a slew of ideas swarmed over me (as things often do). For instance, I'm now receiving better training in the scientific method, learning to interact with my colleagues in a different but very effective manner, and discovering how to ask the right questions at the right times. I'm returning to the basic science roots that feed and nourish the tree of medicine, allowing it to prosper and bear the fruit of health, which today can be eaten by the insured and uninsured alike. But if I had to choose the biggest difference between the lab and the wards, I'd say this: Lab is so much easier, I just can't believe it!

Yes, to reiterate, lab is so easy I just can't believe it. Could this be real? Could I be going in at ten and leaving at four? Am I imagining this or is there really no person (or team) standing over my shoulder evaluating my every move? Am I actually spending my mornings playing *SimCity*® and my afternoons on the Internet discovering how to can preserves and raise cattle? God made the Hebrews wander through the desert for forty years because he wanted the next generation, which had never known slavery, to inherit Canaan, for only they would know how to be free. Now I understand why. For the first few weeks of lab, I didn't know what to do with myself. What do people do between five and seven in the evening if they're not writing notes on patients or catching tuberculosis? I tried to read, but there was nothing I was being forced to learn. I tried napping, but I was too well-rested from my ten hours of sleep the night before. I haven't had this much time to myself since kindergarten, and back then we didn't even have cable.

I remember the first day of lab. I went to lunch with the grad students. Moments after I was seated, I lowered my head and shoveled everything, including several napkins, into my mouth without saying a word. I scarcely left time to breathe, and finished in about two minutes. I looked up to see everyone else still unwrapping their straws, putting ketchup on their hamburgers, and picking the hair out of their deli sandwiches. Long after I had begun to feel the familiar onset of nausea and chills, my colleagues finally finished. But, amazingly, we just sat there, chatting about topics other than bowel movements or attendings. At first, wasting all that time talking made me frantic. I could be getting stuff done, my inner voice kept telling me, even though I wasn't exactly sure what.

Which leads me to another bewildering point—there's nothing in the lab that actually needs to get done. If there are some chest x-rays that need digitizing, they can certainly wait until I've finished my game of backgammon on the Internet. And if I don't finish today, I can do them tomorrow. Or the next day. Or never, because there are no actual results in research, just the process itself. If someone actually answered the questions they were pretending to ask, how could researchers renew their grants for the next five years? Who'd pay for all the pizza at lab meetings?

Perhaps the best part about being in the lab is that there are no patients. No sick people coughing all over me. No methicillin-resistant veterans were aerosolizing their tuberculosis in my direction. No families asking me questions like "What is hypertension?" and "Could you clean up that vomit?" Just my computer and me deriving coefficients for fifth-order fits of various curves. It doesn't pimp me about the renal system and I don't ask it to run too many applications at once. And, at the end of the day, there are no gangrenous toes to wrap.

There are some things I miss from my life on the wards. The friendly wave of the HUC as she forgets to order the stat x-ray on my patient in pulmonary distress. The hearty laugh of the nurse as she records the patient's respiratory rate as "18" for the seven-zillionth time in a row without even looking at him. The funny way his old chart is missing years of hospitalizations for a disease the patient can recall only as "trouble with some enzyme or something." Yes, there are some things that I can't get in the lab. But as I sit in my comfortable rolling chair, listening to the radio and making up data, I wonder if, maybe, I should have gotten a Ph.D. after all.

Physician Heal Thyself

Late Saturday night I had The Dream again. I'm doing my pediatrics rotation and I'm in a hallway lined with a series of rooms. From behind each door comes an unrelenting river of shrieks, like banshees whose souls are being torn apart with pain and misery. Frantic with concern for these poor sick children, I open the first door to find that it's actually a group of residents screaming at each other. Behind each door it's the same until, at some point, they all start pouring into the hall like a flood of demons and begin screaming at me. Strangely, I never see an actual patient.

I woke up suddenly, with not only the usual sweating and chills, but also a weird dizzy feeling and a terribly sore throat. Thankful that I was merely sick and not actually on pediatrics, I wearily began formulating an assessment and a plan. Of course, my first thought was that I should call my mom—she'd know what to do. Which, for someone who is sixteen months away from being a doctor, was exactly the wrong thing to think.

But how do you work up these symptoms? I couldn't remember. If I had gangrenous toes, that would be one thing. If I was sixteen and pregnant with my fourth child, I'd know what to do. But a sore throat and a runny nose? I never really saw any of those on the wards. My first instinct was to order a stat ABG, a magnesium level, and a PTT. But the next draw wasn't until 6:00 A.M. and, even if I made the trip to the hospital, I wouldn't find any nurse actually willing to draw blood, no matter how often it's listed in their contract. So I decided on a six-day course of IV vancomycin, and maybe a chest/abdomen/pelvis CT scan. But even that didn't seem quite right. After all, my in-depth cost-effectiveness training had taught me never to scan anything. Of course, the cost-effectiveness people never really embraced my plan to save the hospital $63,000,000 by treating heart attacks with an alternating regimen of hot and cold baths, either. But that's neither here nor there. What I needed at that moment was some help.

So I turned, as I often do, to my pile of free drugs from my family medicine rotation. I closed my eyes, pulled out some green pills and blue capsules, and washed them down with a pinkish liquid. It made my chest feel a little weird and I saw spots for a while. But, oddly, I didn't feel any better. I thought twenty hours of television might work, but all that did was infect my nutrient-rich couch, so that each new movement is now accompanied by a little splash of wet gram-positivism.

By Monday morning, my body felt it would be best to sleep until noon. When I finally woke up and looked at the clock, I got that terrible sinking feeling in my stomach of horror mixed with panic, darted out of bed toward the shower, then, suddenly, remembered this was my third year, and there was nothing to worry about. Nevertheless, I called the lab and was reassured that no one had even noticed I wasn't there. Satisfied that the field of radiology would survive one more day without the description of the characteristics of hard-to-find pulmonary nodules, I got back into bed.

When my roommate came home, he suggested that perhaps I had a bacterial infection. I certainly couldn't see any colonies of "bacteria" growing on me and I didn't feel little "organisms" running up and down my throat, so I thanked him for the advice with a smirk and went back to sleep. This time I had my other recurring nightmare, the one in which I ask the scrub nurse (whose face is always covered by a surgical mask and who turned out to have a cleft palate) for a date. I needed a cure, fast.

I thought back to my medicine rotation and remembered that a good history and physical could elicit over 90 percent of the correct diagnoses. I hurriedly asked myself a few non-open-ended questions, making sure not to allow myself to start droning on about unimportant crap, and then began my physical. I had just proclaimed myself neurologically intact and begun to feel for nodes when I realized that I didn't really know where to look or even what an enlarged one felt like. Depressed and tired, I gave up, put on my shirt and tie, clipped on my pager, and went to the hospital. Why the fancy clothes? Because that's the only way the nice woman at the pharmacy window would give me a big handful of SEPTRA® tablets. I chose SEPTRA based on how well it, along with a root canal, had recently cured my toothache. And it would be perfect if this turned out to be a urinary tract infection.

I got better within a few days. I'm sure some HMO would say that it was the antibiotic that cured me, but I remain skeptical. I think the symptoms just got bored with such an easy target and left. Either way, I was glad although a bit saddened. For I found out this past week that I don't yet know everything about medicine. After spending an entire year in our tertiary care facility, I don't yet have the feel for treating everyday things, the kinds of problems that friends and relatives will ask me about for the rest of my life, no matter what specialty I choose. As I lay back on my bed, weary from my body's long struggle against its (alleged) microbiologic oppressors, I could find only one thing to give me solace: even at this early stage in my medical training, I think I still know more than the peds residents.

I expect there will be a bidding war between *Radiology* and the *American Journal of Roentgenology* for this poem.

The ABCs Of Radiology

A is for Arteriography, it helps to find bleeding.

B is for Barium, to see if a mass is interceding.

C is for Chest film, PA or AP.

D is for Double-contrast, makes polyps easy to see.

E is for Effusion, Plural's the best.

F is for Fluoro, for a better look at the chest.

G is for Granuloma, which appears calcified.

H is for Hangman's fracture, a cervical collar should be applied.

I is for Ileus, it can be paralytic.

J is for Joints, they can become arthritic.

K is for Kerley B-lines, in congestive disease.

L is for Liver scan, to find metastases.

M is for MRI, of the brain or the kidney.

N is for Nuclear scan, to find a PE.

O is for Overexposure, the film is too black.

P is for Perfusion scan, it's usefulness these lack.

Q is for Quantum, $E=h\nu$.

R is for Radionuclide, in ventriculography.

S is for Sulfur colloid scan, to see if the liver is seeded.

T is for Technetium, a gamma camera is needed.

U is for Ultrasound, to see if anything's off kilter.

V is for Venous thrombosis, give 'em all a Greenfield filter.

W is for Wiener spectrum, frequency versus the square of the power.

X is for X-ray, King Med does about six zillion per hour.

Y is for Yttrium tantalite, its screens emit light in UV.

Z is for Zonography, a narrow-angle CT.

Medicine Is "Grrreat"

Back when I was on my internal medicine rotation, I noticed something about my residents. They were, I found, some of the most intelligent, interesting, dedicated, and enjoyable people I'd ever met. They were well-rounded and fun to be with. They were also crazy.

Each day, my attending gleefully droned on and on about topics like how interesting a workup of decreased pulmonary transpleural pressure could be if one had access to an esophageal balloon-tip catheter, which we didn't. I would nod politely, all the while wondering how these people got this way. They appeared normal, but every once in a while they'd say something like "Hey, we've got a terrific case of malignant ascites coming in—this should be great!" Now, where I come from, the word "great" can have several meanings, but none of them include spending an hour doing an (inadequate) H&P, two hours reading about malignant ascites, and two more hours creating a sixteen-page write-up (copied straight out of Harrison's) that no one ever reads and that never helps the patient get better. I always thought "great" meant sitting in a workroom at the VA hospital doing a crossword puzzle, eating a bagel, and making the occasional long-distance phone call to Denmark.

But it was all my residents could do to keep from skipping and giggling before finishing the sentence. Then came the deluge of "great" articles, each more boring than the last and packed with worthwhile "information" like the fact that four out of six rats tested preferred the taste of ACE-inhibitors to that of calcium-channel blockers. And each article came with that word "great." What was so great about reading articles when I could be doing stuff I liked, such as sleeping or sitting around thinking about sleeping? What had happened to these residents, who seemed normal in every other way, to make them act like this? After all, none of *my* classmates were like that.

Internal medicine eventually ended and third year began. My concerns, like my knowledge of heart disease, started to fade. It was time for my classmates and I to start goofing off, or, more precisely, to start goofing off in a different location—the lab. Everything seemed fine at first. But every once in a while, I'd call someone asking to go out and they'd answer no, they wanted to go to lab that night to start an assay. In the past, many people have made many excuses to keep

80

from hanging out with me. Now, however, I couldn't hear any laughing in the background. After further questioning, nobody could tell me what the word "assay" meant, but they all seemed to think they needed to do one. Well, fine, I reasoned, they probably have a tyrannical principal investigator breathing down their backs. It surely wasn't their fault.

Then a few weeks ago, I was talking with a friend whose name I will not mention (unless someone asks me), and he admitted he really enjoyed doing research. In fact, he was excited about going in every morning and reluctant to leave in the evening. I want to emphasize that this is a normal guy who, I'd believed, had a healthy disdain for work. And he wasn't the only one. Other people I spoke with genuinely seemed to enjoy running gels and packing columns, whatever the hell that is, and felt they were getting more out of their third year than just the opportunity to watch every hockey game that God and the cable company can bring us.

These evenings, my roommate comes home excited about some great journal article discussing the relative merits of bolusing versus the continuous dripping of anti-platelet medications that he had read that day—in his spare time. Once again, there is the incorrect usage of the word "great" to describe his experience. At first, I thought my classmates were still recovering from second year. But the symptoms aren't going away, despite the ZOLOFT® I keep slipping into my roommate's grape juice. I don't know what happened over the last few months. But insidiously, in ways I never imagined possible, my classmates have become *just like the medicine residents*. They're crazy, and there's nothing I can do about it.

Where did we, as a family, go wrong? When did we lose those values we shared as MS-Is that kept our lecture attendance rate hovering at around 30 percent? When did we get sidetracked from our goal of getting through medical school as quickly and as painlessly as possible? Will it be much longer until these people log into the hospital's computer system from home at night to check their patients' magnesium levels? How long until they go in on their rare Sunday off just to "check up on the patients and write a few quick notes"? I'd assumed that my medicine residents had always been like this and that King Med selected for such behavior. But now I'm seeing firsthand that this sort of activity is made, not born. And, frankly, I'm concerned.

To reiterate, the internal medicine residents I know are among my favorite people in the world. I liked being with them immensely, despite my lingering suspicions that they were transported from a distant, yet eerily similar, planet. But I'm beginning to realize that they were once just like me, as evidenced by the slow and inexorable conversion of my once-normal classmates. I can't say I understand what's going on, but I'm willing to blindly accept it, much as I did the fact that the liver causes blood coagulation. However, in exchange, I have one favor to ask. If anyone ever hears me say that I have to go to the lab on a Saturday night so that I can pack a column for the assay I plan to do on Sunday, please wait until I'm not looking and then calmly, but determinedly, kill me.

How Many Lawyers Does It Take . . .

I want to discuss why I don't like lawyers. This is, of course, an unfair generalization. My roommate and good friend is a law student. My date to the med school formal last year is a law student, as is her roommate. I've met several law students whom I like. So what happens when they finish law school and become lawyers? I've given a lot of thought to this question, mainly during agonizing dinner table discussions with lawyers who argue self-righteously about things that aren't important, and about which they're wrong. If I had to put my finger on one sleazy, ill-begotten fact, it would be that the Law is not concerned with the Truth. Quite the contrary, its main concern is hiding the Truth, or distorting it so that its new twisted form can be used mainly for evil. Usually, the easiest means to this end is lying. It's a big game involving first creating arbitrary rules, then seeing who can break them the fastest and in the cleverest way without being caught by twelve people chosen solely because they were unable to avoid jury duty.

Imagine for a moment that doctors took the same approach to their profession. Suppose Mrs. Kaplan walks into her trusted family physician's office with a mild cough and a runny nose. Without even looking at her, her physician says she has pneumonia, prescribes acetaminophen capsules, and charges her $200. "But this doesn't feel anything like pneumonia," sweet Mrs. Kaplan protests.

In response, Dr. Gracilis takes out a pocket camera covered with little sparkles, bells, and gold stars, which he calls his "CAT scanner." He snaps her picture, disappears into the back room, and emerges twenty seconds later with a series of twenty-six images, each with the name "Lee Pinkowitz" hastily scratched out. "This is your pneumonia," he says, pointing to a 7 cm by 12 cm calcified blotch highlighted by barium contrast. Mrs. Kaplan is so scared she doesn't even notice that the patient on the film is missing an arm. "It's worse than I thought. We'll also have to give you AZT in special, uh, paste form. I'll give it to you here so you don't have to go all the way to the mean pharmacist across the street. Just rub this on your chest every, uh, four hours and you'll be fine. If it burns a little, that means it's working. That'll be $3000."

On the other hand, if we didn't have lawyers or other people who were willing to make a career of lying, our system of law would be far less exciting. Trials based on whether or not a person was actually guilty would not only take the romance and drama out of the courtroom, but also prevent guilty people from exercising their legal "right" to get off on a technicality. Imagine what would happen if one of the many King University basic scientists who is forced to spend one month each year teaching med students as a ward attending (despite not having seen a real live patient since before the advent of antibiotics) was to defend a known murderer. By the end of the case, he would have to side with the prosecution, since, after careful examination, he would find the evidence to be against his client, with a "p" value of less than or equal to 0.05.

Thankfully, most physicians operate with an internalized conscience that doesn't allow them to lie and steal from honest, hardworking people. That's for the insurance companies to do. But lawyers seem either to be missing this conscience from childhood or to have lost it along the way. Interestingly, when a patient exhibits this trait, we call him a sociopath or borderline personality. Perhaps in the future we'll just prescribe law school.

Don't think for a moment that such blatant disregard for the Truth is my only complaint against lawyers. It's just the easiest one to fit onto two pages. Other aspects such as the self-righteousness, the need to put image before substance, and the politicking that is "necessary" to become a successful lawyer are all just as bad. It is important to state here that not all doctors are saints, though I believe that the bad ones are in the minority, as opposed to lawyers, for whom dishonesty is part of their job description. What I really think is most important, though, is that nobody shows this book to the cute law student I met at a party a few nights ago.

Congratulations, You've Been Fired

Momentarily forgetting that my cache (as we in the biophysics study track say) of artistic talent amounts to putting those yellow biohazard stickers on bags of normal saline when no one is looking, I decided to sign up for a pottery class. You're probably wondering how I have time in my data analysis-packed day to pursue a subject even less related to medicine than my psychiatry rotation. And that may seem like a logical question to those who've never softened clay to spinning texture with their own sweat and tears. But pottery, as it turns out, is a lot like medical school.

But how, you ask, can throwing an unformed lump of clay onto a cold hard wheel, where it lies helpless and exposed until forces beyond its control cruelly bend and shape it into a new and unrecognizable form, be similar to medical school?

The most obvious answer is that pottery is deceivingly, maddeningly difficult. I imagined pottery class in the East Campus Craft Center would be pretty similar to what I'd seen in the movies, like in *Ghost* when the couple starts working clay on the pottery wheel and ends up making love to the tune of "Unchained Melody." But similar to my discovery about those movies featuring gutsy kids making their way through med school by using only their intelligence, wits, and rugged good looks, I again found that movies don't tell the whole truth. Clay, like med school, can be very, very hard.

"Well Jeff," you might say if you were one of the thousand OR nurses who ejected me from surgery due to contamination, "before I caught you picking wax out of your ear, I saw you do some fine retracting and boveying, and you never once sliced the ureter. I bet you'd be great at the pottery wheel." But you would be wrong. Horribly, horribly wrong.

First, as in med school, the most difficult thing about using the pottery wheel is getting centered. You begin with an idea of where you want the clay to be, but even as you apply all your energy toward getting it there, it starts drifting sideways. As you ease away from the center, your clay becomes less and less well-rounded, until you're left with a crooked, mushy lump, far away from your intended destination.

And nobody tells you about the time commitment. Pottery class, like med school, is not something you do only during certain hours of the day—to be successful, it must become a way of life. Whether you're wearing blood- or clay-stained shoes, you cannot escape the thought that you should study more or spend just one more hour at the wheel. And when you take some time for yourself, there's always that sense of one more bowl uncreated, one more biochemical pathway unlearned.

Furthermore, when you get to class, you expect directed instruction. But as I've discovered time after painful time, class is simply not worth attending. My pottery teacher believes in "letting you discover pottery for yourselves," much as the genetics professors believe in "teaching genetics in such a confusing and disorganized manner that students can't understand a word they're saying, even after asking specific questions about a subject the professors have devoted their entire lives to studying." Eventually I realized it's best to learn from my own mistakes on the pottery wheel as well as with those mice whose genomes I've been trying to alter.

Finally, no matter how distorted and unsatisfactory your final product may seem, it's not complete until it has been hardened by fire. Whether in a kiln or between two peds residents who missed their afternoon naps, only exposure to incredible amounts of heat can prepare clay pots and med students for the life ahead of them. Only after firing can the finished products be relied upon to perform the same action over and over again for the rest of their useful lives, whether it is pouring water or performing gallbladder surgery.

In my case, of course, I still haven't made a pot that successfully holds water. But then again, after three years of fire, I also still haven't learned how to properly diagnose gallstones. Maybe I should've gone to class after all.

Publish Or Perish (I'd Rather Perish)

Since the end of basketball season, I've been searching for something to fill the gaping hole in my life. Home-shopping networks and afternoon talk shows worked at first, but even they became boring, leaving me only with seventeen types of carrot peelers and an intimate knowledge of lesbian dwarves who love their overweight mothers. So I turned my attention in the obvious direction and exhumed my fervent zeal for radiology research; in particular, the thrilling quest to fully describe the characteristics of hard-to-detect pulmonary nodules.

After months of data collection, study design, and rigorous observer training, I finally sat down, made up some numbers that fit into a straight line, and plotted a couple of graphs. I also made several colored pie charts, many of which were labeled. This brought me to the most important step of all—writing my paper.

Writing a paper for an academic journal is not as easy as one might expect. First, your submission has to be at least six or seven pages long. This is difficult when your research data inevitably refuses to show anything more interesting than the fact that *Klebsiella* grows faster on agar containing 10% rather than 9% tryptophan at temperatures less than 289° Kelvin. So what do you do, other than add six different graphs demonstrating the same results? You write out every single word in the most basic, plodding manner possible so that any idiot, or scientist, who reads it is unable to misinterpret anything.

For example, if you wrote a paragraph in your Materials and Methods section for *The Rumanian Journal of Golgi* about how you soaked, dried, resoaked, coated, columnated, iced, shampooed, and then resoaked a protein, you can't complete the paragraph with "and then we ran a Southern Blot on it." No, a more appropriate sentence is: "And then the experimenter, wearing number four La-Tech-brand latex gloves, placed the aforementioned protein, heretofore stored in a polyurethane class 7 BestTube-brand test tube, into the second (2) well of a 1992 Blot-tastic X2799 v2.1 GelRunner for analysis of its glycine to threonine ratio."

Why does it have to be written like this? Because scientists, people who spend most of their lives in small dark labs, apparently without shaving equipment, don't entirely understand the English language. Their bacteria and

87

proteins don't speak English. Their computers talk only in "code." And so their language networks have atrophied over the years, even as their *Star Trek* pathways have grown larger.

After writing a shoddy paper, I gave it to my advisor, who made about a zillion changes, such as replacing every word with three different words. So after I retyped what he had written and handed it back to him, he became convinced that I am the world's expert on hard-to-detect pulmonary nodules. This meant it was time to submit my paper to a journal. But which one? Would *The Annals of Pulmonary Functioning Assessed By Radiograph* be more likely to accept it than *The Milwaukee Confederated Abstracts in Radiology?* Should I send it to the more clinically oriented *Nodule Weekly* or the more scholarly *Academica Radiologica Finlandia?* Since studies have shown that only 1 out of 43 journal articles actually contains something worth reading (+/-6.2 articles, p=0.13), it's hard to know who will accept mine. And, since the editor of *Le Nodule que Pulmonique* hates my advisor because he sent his last article to *Investigative Radiologic Abstracts of Zaire* instead, my options are limited.

Of course, once I make my decision, it doesn't matter where I send it. Inevitably, it will be returned in no more than sixty-seven weeks, rejected because I didn't list in my Results section every number that appeared in Table 16. By the time I resubmit the paper and it actually gets read, seven other experiments will have been published which say exactly the same thing in more words and with prettier graphs. Which is okay, because by then I'll be happily established in my private practice in Boca Raton and paying junior high students to come to my beach house in the afternoons to feed me coconuts and clean my Olympic-sized clover-shaped Jacuzzi by hand.

Sure, for a while, I was discouraged by the daunting publishing process. After all, the progressive educational system at King Med has allowed me to spend twenty, sometimes twenty-five, hours a week learning about the scientific process in between moves of computer backgammon. While students at other medical schools have wasted their whole year learning stuff like pathology and anatomy, I've spent mine receiving a firm grounding in hypothesis development and testing. Why did I need to actually publish?

But after further thought, I realized that this was my big chance to make a difference, to contribute to The Literature. Did I not have a responsibility to the medical profession—to humankind—to share my knowledge of the characteristics of hard-to-detect lung nodules? And so, as we speak, the pages of my article are hurtling toward the editor of *Abstracts in Thoracic Radiology of Oregon.* And if by some crazy chance it does not get accepted, look for my article, "Subtle Pulmonary Nodules Detected on Kodak EX431 Bi-layered SuperGloss Ektafilm Using Silver-riffic III PseudoDeveloper" in a last-minute addition to the appendix of this book.

Honduras, I Hardly Knew Thee

Ah yes, Honduras. So much has happened since then, it almost seems as if I'd never been there . . . as if I'd never been there . . . .

But then the flood of memories comes rushing back as if in a dream. The picturesque mountains capped in a haze of snow and cloud. The arid desert, a four-days' walk with only our provisions and the meat of the armadillo to keep us going. The little children dressed in every color imaginable, as bright as the sun and more energetic. Ricardo and I fighting through the strangling underbrush with only our machetes and our wits, finally emerging into a clearing only to find a fully grown female tiger, beautiful and terrifying, ordering us with her liquid brown eyes to find another route back to the village.

Yes, Central America, much maligned for its political struggles, is a beautiful land. Rich in history, it has nevertheless reached a level of modernity unimagined by the Aztecs. The people, many of whom I grew close to during my stay, take great pride in their country and themselves. Although I didn't know their language, they spoke enough English that we could converse. So I had the opportunity to work with many patients in a far-away country whose medical system is so similar to, and yet so different from, ours.

Major HMOs (whose names translated into Spanish as, literally, "God of Capitation" and "Death by Nurse Practitioner") flourished in the big cities. But in the rural villages where we stayed and worked, they use a crazy system that involves no insurance at all. Rather, patients actually pay for the service they receive! Imagine how primitive a world this is, with no lawyers or actuaries to determine who gets what treatment! And those who have earned money are not forced to pay for the health care of those who didn't! It is thinking such as this that keeps countries like Honduras so far behind the rest of the "civilized" world.

But, despite this, I was able to see several diseases and conditions that I had heretofore only heard about when the internal medical residents generated their four-hour-long differential diagnoses for things as common as ulcers. I was seeing an assortment of odd things, from weird bacterial infections, parasites, and worms to other strange conditions apparently caused by Baal, God of the Heavens. Why Baal would cause these afflictions I don't know (although many attributed it to his battle with Mot, God of the Oceans). But with our extensive third-year medical student training we were able to take various actions, such as asking patients for any pertinent family history and then wrapping their feet in moist gauze. The learning potential was enormous.

Sadly, it was soon time to return to the United States, leaving behind our new friends and the glorious land they inhabited. Yes, Honduras was quite an experience. I have no recollection of how long I spent there—Days? Weeks? When you're that close to the equator, the heat melts time into something liquid, so that in one's memory it can be poured and poured again into containers of any shape. Only the memories remain whole, a reminder of a part of my life that, perhaps . . . was nothing more than a dream. [1]

1. Jeff Drayer did not actually attend the King University Medical Mission to Honduras, but he heard an unending stream of good things about it from those who did.

The Boreds

Before now, it had existed only in whispers and rumors. We talked about it as if it happened to other people, but not to us at King Med. We finished our first year, took our seventeen-hour summer break, and headed onto the wards. A year of catching tuberculosis from veterans, and we were off to the lab. By this time we felt as if we were on the verge of Doctordom, just biding our time until we recited a few oaths and graduated. Basic science had become a pathway-filled memory, saturated with molecules and drug mechanisms long since forgotten. Which is why it came as such a shock to learn that my class would, indeed, have to take the Boards in June.

Yes, the Medical Boards. USMLE Step 1. Like kernicterus in a jaundiced child, it had become ingrained in my brain that after two years at King Med, I was "done." I didn't expect to be doing anything except playing tennis and eating doughnuts for the last two years of med school. I suppose, deep down, I wondered why all those review books were in the bookstore. But I figured they were for people interested in actually knowing something about medicine before they became doctors. As it turns out, though, I also have to know this stuff. I wish someone had told me in advance.

So, after several months of careful thought, I decided to buy some books. "Give me some books," I said to the woman behind the counter, as I slapped a fresh twenty-dollar bill down in front of her. "Review books. As many as I can carry, and keep the change." Her mouth widened to a smile, which turned into a laugh so mocking and disdainful I reflexively held both my hands to my chest, as if to pretend I hadn't contaminated a surgical field or touched something unsterile.

After several minutes of lactic acid build-up, she was forced to stop laughing and hyperventilate. I used the opportunity to explain that I was going to study for the Boards and I needed a couple of basic books to help me brush up.

"Well, which ones do you need?" she asked.

"Uh, I dunno," I replied. "Pathology. Anatomy. That one about how everything, uh, works and . . . stuff."

"Physiology?" she asked, wincing as if just the thought of laughing was enough to make her face hurt. "But which ones?"

Looking back as an experienced review book buyer, I now realize what a good question that was. Because there isn't just one series of review books. You can use the BRS series, or the PreTest series. You can use J&S, Oklahoma Notes, MedMaster, Testastic, Review-a-thon2000, BoarderLine ("The review series with no conscience!"), or Hippocratest ("You'll swear by it!"). But with all those pretty colors, such as orange, and scary titles, such as *Biochemistry*, how does one choose? Well, if one is me, he simply asks the woman at the bookstore to give him her favorites.

"What do you already know?" she asked me. Again, in retrospect, a reasonable question. But hindsight, as I've always said, sucks.

"Well," I answered, "I guess whatever the average third-year King Med student knows about basic science." With that, she began pulling down book after book in a frenzy of blurred colors and flailing limbs. Within moments I could no longer see her behind the stack of books I was holding. It was like carrying a tree.

We got to the counter and she suggested the reasonable price of $1,784. I suggested that rather than pay by the book, I would give up my hard-loaned dollars based on the number of facts I learned. Her face began to twitch again, as she sensed that my suggestion would net the bookstore about thirty-seven cents, and, instead, proposed an installment plan that most loan sharks would have found equitable.

Three hours and forty-eight trips later, I'd lugged every last book into my bedroom. They were neatly piled by subject, alphabetized by author, and stacked from smallest to largest. My room was now more flammable than the oxygen pumped into 95 percent of the VA patients before they go outside to smoke. I was tired and sweaty, but unable to contain my excitement. Because there, surrounding me nearly to shoulder height, I had all the basic science knowledge a doctor could ever need. What radiologist wouldn't love to have the seven steps of cholesterol esterification and transport right at her fingertips? What ophthalmologist doesn't dream of knowing the exact placement and tendonous attachments of the navicular bone? How many oncologists wish they could easily find a list of the nine different layers of a gram-positive bacterium's polysaccharide capsule? It was all here, more basic science than Sir William Osler ever dreamt of, and it belonged to me. With trembling hands, I lifted a pretty green book and gently opened it, braced for a wave of knowledge to break over me.

I imagined I was a multi-legged sponge as I began to race through the first paragraph, soaking up each word about cell membranes. Then I began to stumble over a few of the more difficult words and concepts, such as "phospholipid," "glycerol backbone," and "cell." I reread the paragraph, more slowly this time. Then I tried closing my eyes and visualizing a phospholipid, only I didn't know what one looked like, or even what one was. I kept my eyes closed for a little while longer. And a little longer . . .

The next morning, I swore I'd start studying that evening. I've actually been swearing a lot since then. I know the Boards are still a couple months away. And surely the year I spent staring at ceiling tiles and trying to make anagrams from "oophoriginous" (No sour pig, Ohio) while listening to basic scientists describe the genetic sequencing of the delta protein involved in branching enzyme reactions of sphingomyelin in the lysosome must have taught me something. But, as interesting and useful as that may have been at the time, I have since filled up my brain with other trivia, such as how to manage heart failure, or how to write a sixteen-page admit note that still says absolutely nothing concrete about heart failure.

Nevertheless, I have to fill up my brain again, only to forget everything when I reenter the wards on June 11, where the recital of the seven steps of porphyrin production are about as useful as a tunica vaginalis. Hopefully, in the intervening time I'll find out what, exactly, a phospholipid is.

The Boreds, Part 2

I used to be a well-rounded person. I used to enjoy listening to music, walking outside on sunny days, playing basketball, and reading books. I used to smile, my cheeks red and my eyes bright. I stood up straight, a vibrant person who met every day as a new challenge. I looked at things critically, making my own decisions about the world around me. I was a happy, confident young man.

But that was long ago, in those happy-go-lucky days on the wards when my actions would merely help determine the course of a patient's care or my unsteady hand might only result in a large, painful hematoma. That was before I began studying for the Boards.

Now I sit slumped over my desk, sickly and pale, oblivious to whether it is day or night, warm or cold, anabolic or catabolic. Each new day is like an invincible dragon or a vancomycin-resistant *Enterococcus,* an unbeatable challenge to be survived only so that I may face another. I no longer think for myself; instead, I blindly accept everything I read as truth and expend my energy only in the hope of storing the information in some mental crevice formerly occupied by a baseball statistic. I can only pray it will be retrieved when the crucial moment arrives.

Throughout this forced journey through the labyrinth of medical esoterica, I've used several strategies to try to learn the vast amount of worthless facts so priceless for the Boards. At first, rather than just memorize a list of facts that, if laid end to end, would encircle the earth 178 times, I actually tried to understand each concept so I could intelligently reason out its associated characteristics when the need arose. Needless to say, this lasted about two days; after completing five pages in sixteen hours, I still didn't really understand the concept of a "cell."

The next week I regrouped by watching television and sitting by the pool. I returned invigorated and ready for another try, this time using pneumonics (Latin: *pneumo,* filled with air; *nics,* poorly coached basketball team). After a happy week filled with hundreds of clever sentences, such as "Crafty Mules Never Eat Orange Blouses on Thursdays," I could remember the sentences but not what a single word stood for or which basic principle they were associated with. Time to start again.

But time was running out, and all the hours I spent on the golf course trying desperately to come up with an effective study strategy that incorporated neither understanding nor pneumonics were proving fruitless. I still refused to simply memorize lists of medical facts as long and as interesting (though not as useful) as a Roman census. Finally, I hit upon the idea of staring at each page for four minutes until I could close my eyes and see it imprinted upon my memory like a cartoon on Silly Putty. But I soon realized that just as Silly Putty must be mashed up and rinsed in turpentine to remove the Beetle Bailey newsprint, similarly, I would have to forget the diseases of the ampulla of Vater in order to memorize the diseases of the cystic duct. I was getting nowhere.

Finally, after several days of hard thought—spent lying in bed doing crossword puzzles—I decided to read each review book like a novel, soaking up what I could along the way. This would give me a set of loose associations that I could use heuristically when faced with a question whose answer was not immediately apparent, such as "Where is the spleen?" I followed this plan for a week, speeding through each section of my physiology book with the zeal of someone who knows he will soon catch up to his peers, no longer lagging behind like the external oblique behind a descending testis. But after polishing off physiology in one week and scoring 14 percent on the comprehensive exam at the end of the book, I knew what I had to do.

Now I sit, day after night after day, memorizing lists of facts the lengths of which were heretofore unknown outside of biblical times. My senses have dulled, my muscles atrophied, and my rare conversations, often held with myself, never amount to more than one or two simple sentences, such as, "Give me a pen," "I can't feel my legs," or "Kill me now."

But as black as my days are, the nights are darker still, my dreams rife with horrifying imagery. One night I struggle to escape the strangling confines of a pressure-volume curve even as microorganisms, with and without polysaccharide capsules, lunge and scratch at me with the morbid fervor of mourning Iranians toward a deceased Shah. Another night, a thousand muscles wrap around me in a macabre Kafkaesque fashion, each demanding to know their origin and insertion. I wake up unable to scream, bathed in the same cold sweat I used to get when my parents made me eat lamb.

But the day is coming when my reams of memorized "knowledge" will finally be strewn haphazardly among the answer bubbles of the Boards. I'll once again open my blurred, light-sensitive eyes upon the outside world. I'll slowly assimilate back into society. I'll once again embrace the sound of singing birds as something more than just the signal of an animal whose feces can be a rare cause of tuberculosis.

I suppose there's a lesson to be learned from my experiences, something to be passed down, perhaps in the form of a song or epic poem, from big sib to little sib, from generation to generation. Some readers may have gleaned that it's important to get an early start preparing for the Boards. Others might have learned that each person must tailor their studying strategy to their individual learning style. As for me? I've learned that no matter what happens, you can always retake the Boards in September.

BOOK FOUR

The Skin Game

The Cost-Effective Use of Leeches and Other Musings of a Medical School Survivor

Pros And Consults

Fourth year. After the tireless, painstaking pursuit of medical Truth and pulmonary nodule characteristics, after the constant quest for basic science knowledge for the Boards, I am once again free to roam the wards with the merry abandon of one who no longer must do research or study basic science. But occasional flashbacks to second year remind me that being on the wards entails staying up past my bedtime (9:00 P.M.), writing epic notes, and dealing with more bloody stool than appeared in the med school brochure. It was with some trepidation, therefore, that I reentered the world of clinical medicine.

In the lab, when I didn't understand something, or even when I did, I could just ask a grad student and he'd do my work for me. I never had a single worry. But the wards are a very different world. I don't remember how to write orders. I can't recall what, let alone how many, things are included in a Chem-7. So the first day, when my dermatology resident handed me a pink piece of paper and told me to do a consult on Room 8123, I was more than a bit hesitant, and not just because I didn't remember where Room 8123 was. But the one thing I did remember from second year was never to admit when I didn't know something. So I headed toward the hospital, equipped only with my stethoscope, a clipboard, and a vague concept of what a vesicle was.

When I arrived, I wasn't quite sure what to do, so I thumbed through the chart for a few minutes, trying to appear as though I was getting some important information from the patient's dietary restrictions. But as hard as I looked, I couldn't find any dermatology notes. Then I realized that *I was Dermatology,* and they expected me to provide some kind of specialized information. Calling upon my firm grounding in patient relations provided by Clinical Arts, I decided that the appropriate step at this point in the consult was to go in and actually talk to the patient.

What I had forgotten about the internal medicine floors was that most of the patients were too sick to bother remaining conscious, and the woman in Room 8123 was no exception. She was, as far as I could tell, simply a small woman connected to an enormously swollen pair of legs. I stood there for several moments as a soft, drowsy voice began to mumble inside my head. "You're doing a consult . . . on the dermatology service . . . dermatologists deal with the skin . . . this patient has some skin." Skin! That was it! Ignore the swelling, the pitting, and the weeping—just check for a macule or something. Happy to have a specific task, I examined her face for weird-looking spots. Sure enough, there was a mole. On this septic, cirrhotic, stuporous, thrombocytopenic, arthritic, asplenic woman with congestive heart failure, I had found a mole. Time to start writing it up.

I took out my trusty ruler and began to measure the area on her cheek when I heard from the doorway, "So, are you gonna wrap them?" No particular answer came to mind, since I couldn't see how the word "them" referred to a single mole, let alone why someone would want to wrap a mole in the first place. I stared dumbly at the medicine resident in the doorway until she had to ask again, "Are you gonna wrap them?"

It was clear that staring at her wouldn't make her go away. Didn't she know I had to measure this thing and write it up so I could get back in time for the drug company-sponsored free lunch?

"Are you Dermatology?" she asked, trying to communicate with my slack, frozen countenance. When it nodded, she continued more slowly, with emphasis, "Then are you going to have to wrap them? Her legs?" Suddenly, the prospect of explaining why I was measuring the woman's face seemed a very real, very uncomfortable possibility. I had to get rid of the resident. What should I do? Pretend not to have gotten to that part of the exam yet? Fake a seizure? My ability to lie on demand had atrophied during my year away from the wards. But I had to remain in control. Always look like you know what you're doing. Which is why, though my stupefied facial expression never changed, when my dry lips slowly parted to release a guttural, gravelly "Y-e-e-s-s-s," I was pleased to see the resident nod her head, issue a quick thanks, and walk off down the hall.

Very happy with myself for completing a successful consult, I began to pack up my things when my beeper went off. It was my resident, wanting to know what we needed to do with Room 8123. "Wrap 'em," I said confidently. "We've gotta wrap 'em."

"Sure," he agreed. "How come?"

My mind began slogging through the maze of recently acquired basic science. While I could have named the origin of every atom in a pyridine ring, the only explanation for what I wanted to do to this patient was the softly-spoken, hesitant half-question, "Edematous?"

"All right—go ahead and wrap," exclaimed my pleased resident. "Just remember, first the zinc, then the coban." Click.

Zinc? Co-what? Needless to say, the next hour could translate into a tale as long, complicated, and violent as a treatise on the Battle of Antietam, but with more oozing legs. Rather than describe what happened in that room, lest the authorities choose to use it as "evidence," let's see, instead, what we can learn from this episode. My derm resident should learn never to trust a King Med student coming back to the wards after a year of research. The medicine resident should learn not to trust a guy who represents the Dermatology department but still doesn't know the difference between a macule and a pustule. The patient should learn to go to the private community hospital. And finally, the makers of zinc wrap should include a warning label stating that it is indeed possible to attach one's stethoscope to a patient's leg with their product, and that even unconscious people not only think that stuff tastes awful but also can experience difficulty breathing through it.

And what did I learn, besides the fact that zinc wrap is not easy to remove from moist surfaces? I learned that life in the hospital, even doing consults, isn't simple. The subspecialists must know a lot of specialized information to provide appropriate patient care. And perhaps most important of all: no matter how ill-prepared you are, there is no event too complex and no procedure so difficult that you can't simply blame the disastrous results on the nursing staff.

Movie Madness

Once again, it's time for one hundred new smiling faces peeking out from behind one hundred shiny new laptops to begin to realize their lifelong dream of becoming a doctor. And why shouldn't they smile? After all, they've seen every movie about med school sixteen times, yearning for the day when they too could study 173 hours a week in the noble pursuit of the power to heal. And the movie characters always made it through. Most of them even got the girl and managed to stay at the top of their class despite spending two hours a day riding their motorcycle and "breaking all the rules." Almost all had stony jaws.

But if we've learned anything from the *Star Wars* trilogy, it's that, as realistic as they may seem, life does not always imitate the movies. The movies use "special effects" to make biochemistry look interesting. Most of the actors wear "makeup" to make them look like they understand the renal system. Often, the writers of the movie "lie" to make medical students look cool. Which is why I, as the voice of reason, want to ensure that everyone's expectations don't get too far out of whack, a condition which, if left untreated, has been known to cause hemorrhage.

First of all, med school actually lasts for four, five, or, if you're so insecure that you need a Ph.D., thirteen years rather than ninety minutes. When you become bored with the movie after seventy-five minutes, you only have fifteen to go, whereas when you become bored with med school after seventy-five minutes, you still have 2,108,085 left. And that doesn't include the time you spend during your internship restudying for the Boards, which you failed during third year.

On the other hand, the amount of time movie stars spend in gross anatomy is a pretty good approximation of how long we spend in anatomy at King Med— between eighteen and forty-two minutes. Unfortunately, the actors and actresses come out with a better understanding of whatever the hell's going on in the pelvis.

Another misconception we get from movies is that studying, while grueling and tiring, builds character, gains you respect, and, in the end, makes you feel good about yourself. In life, however, this occurs about as often as a guaiac-negative veteran. Studying sucks the life out of you, leaving you a dry, withered husk dreaming of the days when you were filled with the sweet yellow corn of life.

No one in the movies ever brings home their bone box.

In the movies, students make life-saving decisions as routinely as most people sneeze, and their acute clinical acumen and solid, take-charge attitude result in the gutsy heroics that brings audiences to their feet. The only life-saving decision you could possibly make in med school is whether to kill the cockroach crawling across your chest as you lie in the eighth floor call room explaining to the nurse who paged you at 3:38 A.M. that your written order "TYLENOL for pain" means that yes, she may give TYLENOL tablets for this patient's pain and, yes, a headache counts as pain. Of course, even if you did make a life-saving decision as a med student, it would first have to be co-signed by your resident and then discussed for thirty-five minutes with your attending before the HUC could ignore the order for three hours.

In the movies, med students never get screwed by the OB/GYN course director.

The lecturers in the movies are lifeless M.D.'s who drone on about medical topics. In med school, the lecturers are Ph.D.'s who drone on about topics only peripherally related to medicine and which they have researched for seventeen years, such as why rabbits deprived of their BK68H:R16q gene and exposed to 20,000 times the normal yearly dose of ultraviolet light take seven hours less to heal from a laparoscopic, rather than an open, cholecystectomy.

Don't get me wrong. There are plenty of things a first-year med student can look forward to. For example, savoring the knowledge that for twenty unforgettable minutes of your life you were able to recite all the steps in the malate shunt. Or good-naturedly weathering the whiny screams of "overworked" pediatrics residents. You can anticipate adding to The Literature in your third year by presenting your poster, titled "The Antigenic Properties of Fungus F4GX:3.7 in a Hairless Groundhog Model for the Purposes of Creating Sporulating Colonies Refracted in Red or Green Light," at the Connecticut Society for Research in Unicellular Immunity's annual convention. And, you will eventually reap the hard-earned reward of $62,000 a year, before taxes.

So why not smile? Your whole life was a prelude to this moment. Soon you won't even remember what it was like to have free time or to feel the sun striking your skin. You'll come to accept everything that goes on in med school as normal and you'll even develop a tolerance to it, as one does to nicotine. And when all the work, the lack of sleep, and the constant feelings of inadequacy start to get to you, just make some popcorn, fire up the VCR, and tell yourself over and over again that, indeed, it really is just like in the movies.

The Skin Game

Greetings from Boston! As graduation looms, my classmates and I are trying to decide where to apply to do our residencies. This becomes difficult because *(a)* most of us really don't want to do a residency and *(b)* we don't know anything about the programs we're applying to. Therefore, I've taken it upon myself to investigate some of the more popular hospitals to which King Med students apply. My assignment for this month is Bay State General. When it turned out that King Med had not procured my suite at the Ritz-Carlton for the month, I settled in on my friend Mark's floor and began my assignment. So as not to alert anyone as to my real mission, I quietly disguised myself as a fourth-year medical student on the dermatology rotation and began my study. Here is the shocking story of my month in Boston.

Stiff-necked and sore, I arose from the floor and took the two-hour ride into the hospital, moistly packed into a subway car with a scantily-clad mass of sweaty body parts which I later realized comprised several hundred dermatology patients. After arriving and smearing myself with antibacterial cream, I found the conference room and met my fellow students. Although they were pale and didn't have funny accents, what really struck me was that they were incredibly agreeable, friendly, and interested in everything going on around them, much like their counterparts at King Med. For instance, every last one of them was seriously thinking about a career in dermatology and, as it turned out, each was very interested in working in the clinic that just happened to be staffed by the chair of the department. In addition, they were all very interested in helping the chief resident carry her bag and slide projector to her car. This surprised me, since I knew how excited they were to start reading the assigned journal articles on dermatology, which they thought looked "fascinating," "exciting," and "very fascinating."

Soon I was off to the clinic, which I warmly refer to as ACC-489, where I was to spend the next twenty-eight days. To my surprise, the residents were not wearing military dress and the attendings didn't walk around with rifles and foaming, bloodthirsty hounds on leashes the way it had been described to me. As the first week passed, I began to see that these folks were rather normal, and by that I mean as normal as any resident or attending who goes into a specialty

104

associated with internal medicine: They were obsessed with their patients, meticulous to the point of contracting an ulcer over spelling errors, and had file cabinets seventeen feet long full of The Literature. But after I got to know them, I realized that their differential diagnoses were no longer, their liquid nitrogen no colder, and their orders written no more illegibly than ours at King Med.

As I lay awake on my friend Jay's couch the Friday night after my first week, I began to think. Maybe the people here were the same as those at King Med. Maybe the same, even, as doctors everywhere. I shuddered and lapsed into a cold, dreamless sleep.

The rotation has gone as I expected, with lots of diseased skin pleasantly interspersed with diseased mucous membranes. My days are full of rashes, which are all treated with cream, as well as bumps, which are all cut off. My nights are spent both finding a relatively clean bed where I won't be arrested and thinking about the medical profession. Why is it that we make such a big fuss about which hospital someone trained at, whom they did their research with, and how well-recognized their letter-of-recommendation writers are?

As I spiked a volleyball into the chest of the department chair at the departmental picnic, I recognized his expression of surprise and dismay as the same one that would be worn by any doctor in the same situation. But, as I passed a student who was telling the head of the residency selection committee that she really thought dermatology was right for her for a number of reasons and could she, perhaps, list some of them for him now, and, well, then could he maybe tell her about some of his many interesting experiences from his long and distinguished career in dermatology, I realized where the big fuss comes from. And in four years when she's the chief resident, nobody will be surprised—and so the cycle will continue.

I've learned a lot here in Boston, some of it skin-related, some not. Much of it I had always suspected, but I needed to travel somewhere else to know for sure. But late each night, as I wander through the urology floor searching for an empty room where I can lay my aching frame until the nurses discover me and throw me out, I see a hospital to which a doctor could become accustomed, even grow to love, much like King Med. Much, in fact, like any hospital.

Sub-I Of The Tiger

I just got off my medicine subinternship (sub-I). The premise of the sub-I is that med students act in much the same manner as interns, except without needing to possess all that bothersome medical knowledge. For some reason, I decided it would be worth a month of my life to learn how to function as a house officer, carrying a few patients in the same way I had done throughout second year, except that now, my orders had to be co-signed by the resident rather than the intern, except when the resident wasn't around, in which case the intern, who knew more about my patients than I did, would co-sign them anyway.

I'll admit I was nervous. I wondered just what a house officer did and whether I had what it took to make a good one. Could I handle the pressure of making instant life-or-death decisions? Could I think on my feet fast enough, incorporating the useful information and ignoring the superfluous, to formulate a plan of action for any situation I encountered? Could I bear the enormous amount of responsibility associated with caring for the human lives entrusted to me? After only a few days of observing how interns spend their time, I realized, to my relief, that it wouldn't be too hard after all. Because, basically, an intern is nothing more than an underpaid secretary who works a zillion hours a week.

The first day of my sub-I, I sat in the workroom playing computer solitaire and waiting for a medical emergency to arise. Suddenly, after only four hours, there it was: Mrs. Reisman needed home health care! But she was being discharged that day—and the social worker hadn't seen her yet! The tension was palpable, but I leapt into action and called the social worker. She patiently explained that she could not see my patient until the next day, since she had only two hours notice and would be leaving promptly at 5:00 P.M. Three hours and 1,066 phone calls later, I had arranged for Mrs. Reisman to have her vitamins delivered to her on a weekly basis. Crisis avoided.

But, just like a real intern's day, mine was far from over. After Mrs. Reisman had left the floor, my resident casually asked if I had arranged her follow-up appointment. Didn't the hospital hire people to do that sort of scut work, I asked? People like social workers, nurses, or P.A.'s? Two hours and only 43 phone calls later, Mrs. Reisman had a follow-up appointment.

106

And so my day continued, similar to my time as a camp counselor twelve years ago, only with more drool. Finally, everybody had left and it was just my team and the patients. I was on call. This was the time when my mettle would be measured, when we'd see if I could look pressure in the eye and diagnose it. But, after two hours of tracking down lost pathology results and forty-five minutes trying to get one of my patients downstairs for a stat chest x-ray, I began to lose hope. When midnight rolled around and it was obvious nothing was going to happen, I went into the call room and fell asleep—I think.

I'm not sure just what happened during the next seven hours. Every time my pager went off, I was newly confused. The first time, after I banged on my alarm clock, tried to figure out why there was a fire drill, and attempted to check my laundry, I finally realized that the noise was my pager. I returned the call, breathlessly anticipating a medical dilemma that only someone with my years of training could solve. I was already half-dressed when the nurse on the other end told me that Mr. Wang's blood pressure was 175/90. I raced out of the room, throwing on my jacket and stethoscope, already forming a plan of action. Diuretics? Beta-blockers? Emergency valvuloplasty? I was there in seconds. I listened to the patient's heart as I checked his pulse. Yes, this was trouble. I grabbed the chart to check his last set of vitals, and was shocked to find he had been in the 180s for two weeks. The nurse, noticing the look of utter confusion on my face, told me that indeed, this was his baseline blood pressure. She just thought I'd want to know.

I'm rarely interested in abnormal blood pressures, even during the daytime. So, with a scowl reminiscent of nineteenth-century literary villains, I left the floor and went back to sleep. But that was only the first of 23 calls from the nurses that night, ranging from requesting some acetaminophen for a patient to informing me that a patient's brother wanted to talk with my intern tomorrow. Each time the pager went off, I was shaken by a new stroke of terror, a new haze of confusion.

To be fair, there was the occasional medical situation that needed attention. For these, I determined my plan and then called my intern, just to make sure I was doing the right thing. My intern would agree with my plan but then, as anyone in internal medicine is apparently forced to do to become certified, he stood outside the patient's door for forty-five minutes groaning, shaking his head, and wondering whether he did the right thing. After watching him go through this the first two times, I learned to excuse myself after five minutes since nothing ever came of it. Besides, the nursing home placements had tired me out and I didn't feel like doing a $3000 workup, eighteen cultures, and seven fundal exams every time the nurse found a drop of drool on a patient's pillow.

In the end, I learned a great deal from my medicine sub-I. Of course, I still can't tell the difference between all those goofy-sounding antiarrhythmics. Nor do I know what "prerenal" means. I don't even know how to do a good physical exam or assess whether a patient needs to go to the intensive care unit. Why? Because interns don't deal with those things. They run around all day doing paperwork and chasing down test results. So what *did* I learn? I learned that it takes a lot of hard work, patience, caring, and the willingness to go to any lengths for your patient to be a good intern. But, fortunately for me, it doesn't take much at all to be a bad one.

Drayer Does Dallas

Hello from the Texas Women's School of Nursing dormitory! My month in Dallas has been terrific, although it is quickly drawing to a close. The memories will, as memories sometimes do, stay with me forever. And some of them will be sweeter than others. For example, I'll always remember spending a month's rent at the Texas State Fair, dating a *Hooters* waitress, playing countless rounds of golf, and watching two girls fend off Emmitt Smith to save me a seat at a bar. But those will never equal what will always remain my fondest memory of this wonderful city: an entire month spent working at a private hospital.

Up until a few months ago, I didn't know there was such a thing as a private hospital. I thought every hospital was like King Med—the same lazy employees, the same terrible schedules, and the same eerie smells. But a friend told me of a land, not too far away, where residents were more than just secretaries. There was a place, she told me, where patients paid for their medical care. Where some patients came to the ED for reasons other than being drunk, out of heroin, or too lazy to make a doctor's appointment. She called this place Utopia University Hospital. It sounded so magical, so otherworldly, I simply had to see it, if only to prove that it wasn't true. But, it was true, so very wonderfully true.

It began the very first day. I needed some blood from a patient and so, as always in a new blood-drawing situation, I tried to locate a needle and syringe, alcohol, gauze, test tubes, a tourniquet, and the nearest resident for when I missed on the first three tries. I looked everywhere but couldn't find anything, so I decided to ask someone for help. Given my ingrained terror at the prospect of speaking to or, worse, asking a question of an HUC, I gingerly sought out the "floor coordinator" (Utopia's HUC equivalent), believing that, as usual, I would be severely burdening an overworked individual who could not possibly eat doughnuts, complain about the long hours, and answer my question at the same time. However, I was unable to find any grossly overweight person eating hamburgers while yelling at her kids over the phone. Instead, the floor coordinator was an ordinary person who cheerfully told me that I didn't need to draw any blood—the patient's nurse would take care of that.

That moment was, perhaps, the happiest of my medical school career, even though I was so overcome with shock that my brain was unable to register any emotion at all. My blank stare of incomprehension belied the joy and wonder that came later after I had fully digested the information. Did this average-size floor coordinator mean that a nurse was actually going to draw blood? That the very thing that has defined the role of nurses throughout time was going to actually be done by a nurse rather than by a medical student or resident? My neural wiring was unprepared for this and it took me several days to recover. But that was only the beginning.

Only two days later, I realized something was missing. Where were those four-hour blocks of time spent sitting in a room with thirty other people and pretending to be interested in the latest study of collagen vascular disorders using hedgehog embryos soaked in laminin? I hadn't been to a single conference yet. All I did was see patients and get my work done. What was going on here?

The obvious answer was that the residents here were not forced to attend seventeen crucial meetings every morning, ranging from the Jejunum Conference to the Pancreatic Secretions Conference. How could these people take care of patients, I wondered, without attending a weekly Thoracic Duct Conference? How could they understand anything about sweating disorders without attending Sebaceous Rounds? Somehow, though, they were learning medicine.

Maybe it was because they were able to get their work done, do some reading, and get enough sleep, instead of sitting through four miserable hours of rounds every morning mindlessly generating differential diagnoses the length of the "Goldman" listing in the Brooklyn White Pages. Or maybe it was because when there was a conference, a drug company provided food rivaling a thirteenth-century French monarchical banquet, just as God meant for it to be. Whatever the reason, the residents seemed happy and extremely good at what they did. I simply didn't know what to make of it.

Another thing became more noticeable with each passing day: I only saw hospital employees when they were doing their jobs. The janitors cleaned things up and the food services people prepared food for the patients. No one stood with their linen carts or "Rush—Blood Materials" coolers watching the elevators come and go as they chatted endlessly about church last Sunday. No guys leaned on their brooms and debated whether Dennis Rodman is the coolest basketball player in the world, or the coolest person in the world. You didn't even need to promise your first-born child to get a stat x-ray. Nope, at Utopia, the employees seemed to do their jobs the entire time they were getting paid. And they did them well, since the hospital was beautiful, spotless, and fairly efficient. Then it occurred to me—perhaps at private hospitals the administrators are actually allowed to fire people if they're not doing a good job! Maybe they don't have to wait for a "good" reason, like armed robbery or manslaughter, before they can fire someone without fear of a gigantic lawsuit or a labor strike. This place was looking better and better.

So, it is with just a touch of ambivalence that I prepare to return to King Med. I'll miss the friendly patients and the competent staff at Utopia. I'll really miss not having a parking spot twenty yards from my clinic. But, after all, King Med is the place where I grew up. It's the place that taught me to order as many tests as I could think of so as not to miss any of the sixty-eight possible diagnoses for right arm pain following a motorcycle accident. It's the place where I know that a recalcitrant patient can be lured back to his oxygen mask with a pack of cigarettes. And it's the place where I can spend a whole day on a rotation trying to find housing for a woman who leaves every nursing home placement within forty-eight hours. Once I return, we'll talk about what's going on at Hopkins and did you hear who the new chair is at the Brigham, and so forth. They'll tell me I need a solid academic program for my internship, particularly if I want to get into a fellowship, blah, blah, blah. But they can't make me forget what I've seen— they can't take away my memories. After all, I saw a nurse draw blood from a patient.

Hopefully, this will soon appear in *Annals of Internal Medicine* as my tribute to "Green Eggs and Ham."

Green Sputum And Phlegm

I do not like breathing
To be so hard.
I do not like my lungs
All black and charred.

I would like to erase
My oxygen debt.
I would like to have
One more cigarette.

I do not like
Chronic bronchitis.
I do not want
M. catarrhalis.

I could not bring back
My alveoli.
I could not with
A good MDI.

I would not like
Skin that's colored gray.
I would not cut down
To just 2 packs per day.

I could not breathe
Even in a steroid mist.
I deserve to move up
On the transplant list!

I would not, could not
Walk up stairs.
I would not, could not
Prevent these flares.

I would not, could not
Raise my FEV.
I would not, could not
Like COPD.

I do not like
Green Sputum and Phlegm.
Oh, why am I cursed
With such a bad problem?

In The Joint

I don't know what possessed me to spend four weeks on rheumatology. Maybe it was the allure of seeing elderly patients with extremely painful, extremely incurable diseases. Possibly, it was the opportunity to experience a level of learned helplessness surpassed only by psychiatry for being able to neither diagnose nor help any of their patients. Perhaps it was morbid curiosity as to why these patients continue return to their rheumatologists despite the irrefutable facts that their joint pain never gets better and their rheumatologist-prescribed non-steroidal-analgesic-induced GI bleeding gets worse? Undeniably, the filters that normally suppress my self-destructive urges were missing, or else they were preoccupied with preventing me from stalking Drew Barrymore.

Rheumatology, it turns out, is as boring as dirt. But if you have a problem with dirt, you can hire somebody to sweep it. If you have a rheumatological disease, however, you can give it 18 different non-steroid preparations, run 586 different blood tests, press your thumbs against all 324 joints, and still not know what the problem is.

The entire purpose of the "specialty" of rheumatology is to order an erythrocyte sedimentation rate (sed-rate) on every patient that walks in the door. This is amazing, since the sed-rate is about the least useful test employed by doctors since phrenology. The only significance of a positive sed-rate is that it tells the doctor the patient has a positive sed-rate. It's too non-specific to rule anything out and too untrustworthy to rule anything in. Which is why, after you've gotten your positive, or negative, sed-rate and you're unfortunate enough to be a rheumatologist, you then put your patient on a non-steroidal drug.

Now, these are good medications because they combine the ineffective analgesia of aspirin with the poor anti-inflammatory effects of acetaminophen. And sometimes they do not cause bleeding ulcers. But the real advantage of these drugs is that they don't contain steroids. Therefore, when they don't work, the next step is to put the patient on steroids. This usually alleviates some of the patient's joint pain, mainly because they are soon preoccupied with their atypical infections, paper-thin skin, and brittle bones. It's at this point that the rheumatologist refers the patient back to her family practitioner, orthopedist, P.A., or anyone who will take her, since she now has too many medical problems

114

to be considered a rheumatology patient. She is then usually admitted to the hospital.

To be fair, rheumatology is not just clinic-based. There are times when other physicians need advice concerning their hospitalized patients with joint symptoms or a strange connective-tissue disease. Then the rheumatologist is consulted and has the chance to shine in front of his colleagues, the chance to prove that the extra two-year fellowship was not, in fact, the biggest mistake of his life. In such difficult cases, the rheumatologist takes an hour-long detailed history from the patient, performs a complete physical exam, carefully documents everything in the chart, and then orders a sed-rate. In especially complex cases, he might use his specialized training to also order an anti-nuclear antibody test or, if the consulting physician believes the patient might have lupus, a lupus panel. Thereafter, he happily removes himself from the case, telling everyone that he'll be glad to explain the significance of the sed-rate results if they have any questions.

But what rheumatologists lack in actual medical effectiveness they make up for by their ability to sit and talk about uninteresting drivel with patients for hours on end. Every morning, my worn spirits are lifted when I see only seven patients on the schedule for the entire day. Eight agonizing hours later, however, we are still talking to nice Mrs. Daugherty, who is number 3 on the list, about her grandson's weasel collection. Meanwhile, my blood pressure has stabilized at 230/145 and my forehead veins are bulging sufficiently to perform dialysis through.

But, of course, this is the reason the patient is there in the first place—to have someone to talk to. Eighty-five percent of rheumatologic diseases are what we cleverly refer to as "fibromyalgia," which is actually Latin for "pain in crazy people." There's nothing wrong with these patients' joints that can be treated. They're just people who can afford to pay a rheumatologist's fees to receive the services of a social worker. And every rheumatologist knows that they have to be nice to these people, change their dosage of non-steroidals every once in a while, and occasionally admit them for bleeding ulcers. Because without these patients, they couldn't continue to practice a specialty in which there aren't many diseases they can actually treat.

So I guess I'll finish up my month here, shuffling around like a zombie until someone finally lets me off this rotation. Then, once again, I'll rest my weary frame on the couch, stop pretending I have any idea what a pannus formation is, take a couple of NSAID capsules, and then sleep until my ulcer acts up.

Secrets And Lies

I entered medical school believing that, as a doctor, my job would be to collect the pertinent facts about the patient, synthesize them into a list of possible diagnoses, selectively run tests to narrow the list, and then choose from among the available treatment options. It sounded like a pretty good job, one that I could do for the rest of my life and that would make me relatively happy. But what they didn't tell me when I applied was that those activities are actually secondary to what turns out to be a doctor's principal job: Determining whether or not your patient is lying.

Or at least that's what it seemed like at first. But studies now show that, in fact, all patients lie. The doctor's primary job is to figure out exactly which parts of their history and physical they're lying about. Listening to the patient, we're always led to believe that they have never done anything that could have contributed to their current condition, such as smoking, drinking, or placing things into orifices they were not meant for. "How do you explain the presence of a twelve-inch lizard skeleton in this x-ray of your transverse colon?" I once asked a patient. He simply could not imagine. And so on.

Of course, this presents a big problem. How can we successfully treat patients who won't give us the information we need to make an accurate diagnosis? It's bad enough that my time *and* tax money are going toward their medical care so that they can return to their jobs, such as heroin dealer, and once again enjoy their hobbies, such as heroin addiction. But if patients won't even tell me their problem, it becomes much harder to fix, especially since I'm too lazy to spend a lot of time figuring out what it is.

In today's world of cost-effective medicine, patients' lying costs the health care system more than every other factor combined, except for those $40,000-a-day oxygen tents that outraged talk-show fans insist we use in the hopes of miraculously curing terminally ill babies. So I've been doing a little thinking lately. It seems to me that if we could somehow see through the lying, we could help these patients despite themselves, thereby saving the health care system enough money for HMO presidents everywhere to acquire a personal Learjet. And after careful examination, I believe I have the answer. My plan may initially put a financial strain on the system, but in a few short months, we should begin to reap the enormous benefits. Best of all, the plan is simple, and can be implemented by both the largest academic center and the smallest community hospital in just a few weeks. What is this fantastic plan that will revolutionize health care? *Equip every hospital room with a lie detector.*

This will change everything. Guessing how much alcohol "two beers a night" represents will become a thing of the past. No more pregnancy tests on teenage girls who insist they've never had sex. Patient histories, instead of grueling two-hour marathons at the VA, will become an easy ten-minute exercise. Since all the answers to simple yes/no questions will be true, I'll never have to ask another open-ended question again.

Under this System of the Future, no longer will we have to drag answers out of patients in Clinical Arts-esque fashion. Instead, future conversations with patients will go much like this:

"Now Mrs. Stockton, you say that your wrist pain started yesterday afternoon during a work-related incident."

"Yes."

"Did it really begin hurting for the first time yesterday afternoon?"

"Yes" (Beep Beep!)

"Mrs. Stockton . . ."

"It did!" (Beep BEEP!)

"Did this have anything to do with getting drunk over the weekend and walking into a sliding glass door?"

"No." (BEEP BEEP!)

"Mrs. Stockton, are you really here just to get workman's compensation?"

(BEEP! BEEP! BEEP!)

This new system will be a godsend. Of course, there will be those fruitcakes who insist that lie detectors curtail freedom of speech, therefore infringing upon patients' rights. But my question is, which right? The Right to Lie to Your Doctor? If patients really want to get better but refuse to hold up their end of the bargain by not doing everything in their power to get better, then they don't deserve our help. Perhaps it would be just as well if they sought out some alternative type of health care, such as crystals, roots, or P.A.'s.

Yes, I believe this innovation will solve many of our current problems. People will be healthier than ever, more federal money can be funneled into retrials for convicted felons, and call nights will become synonymous with a good seven hours of uninterrupted sleep. To this end, I plan to contact various manufacturers of lie detectors and initiate the inevitable bidding war for the right to provide the hardware for my plans. Of course, I still have a few months of medical school to go, so I'll be too busy squeezing out as much learning as I can to think about the Jacuzzi I'll be buying with my first royalty check from the lie detector company (BEEP BEEEP BEEEEEEEP!!!).

117

Apply Yourself

"You should hire a secretary."

Those words ring in my ears, the parting advice from one of my friends off to his internship. I heard him, but as with most advice I get from people other than my astrologer, such as "you should attend microbiology" and "you should take the hamster out of the microwave," I didn't listen. After all, I had completed a medicine subinternship, thus proving I could do secretarial work with the best of them. And so, it will be the historians' job to assess just how much damage I did to my chance of acceptance when, of my own volition, I undertook the residency application process on my own.

How hard could it be? I figured I would just type my name and address, answer a few questions, print out my personal statement, and send it all in. No problem. I just needed to *write* a personal statement.

This was easier said than done. Because it turns out that the purpose of the personal statement is to tell the residency committee about yourself in as bland and nondescript a manner as possible, so as not to insult anyone. Although bland and nondescript happen to be two of my specialties, I couldn't seem to compose anything that didn't sound, well, stupid. No matter how I put the sentences together, my statement seemed to be written by someone whose medical school record contained no evidence suggesting he had ever wanted to be a dermatologist.

Finally, after composing the most boring self-description possible, throwing in a few selected plagiarisms from Goethe, and buying $186.27 worth of beige paper, my personal statement was complete.

Which led me to the next step: creating a curriculum vitae, which is Latin for "Sheet of Lies." Almost miraculously, I became the most well-rounded, extracurricular person alive. Understandably, people were skeptical, since most of my time in med school has been spent asleep. But I assured everyone that I was indeed King Med's representative to the United Legion of Medical Centers and, in fact, the emperor of the Eastern Regional Future Skin Care Providers Association. And if my lawyer knows as many stalling tactics as he says, Match Day will have come and gone before anyone can prove differently.

With those two major obstacles behind me, it was time to put together the actual applications. First, I had to type my name, address, birth date, social security number, and past legal offenses on each of the thirty-six applications. Thirty-six times I typed out my mother's maiden name and my reasons for being thrown out of the military, each time either slightly above or below the line indicated, despite my constant attempts to line everything up with my fingernail.

Then came the section of the application in which, even though they know I just spent all my free time in the past month coming up with a personal statement that doesn't sound entirely fake, significantly exaggerated, or outright false, they would still like me to answer a few questions, such as where I see myself in ten years, what honors I've received, and whether I have a conflict with interviewing on Thanksgiving Day. It took another several weeks to answer these, including the time it took the programs to send me another application because I misjudged just how few words actually fit in the three lines provided and therefore could not squeeze in that I was vice-president of the National Academy of Egyptian Medical Students.

Next, I had to get my transcripts, which necessitated selling my car and taking out another loan. Once I got them, I found out that some of my second-year clerkship grades were still pending and that the clerkship director was "working on it." (Un)fortunately, my OB/GYN grade was there. The transcript business took only several weeks to straighten out, as various administrators continued their seemingly unending campaign to prevent me from doing a residency.

In the meantime, I needed a different personal statement to send to my preliminary year internal medicine programs. After assuring them that I was very interested in obtaining a strong background in internal medicine, I thought I was finished. What I hadn't realized was that since I was applying to transitional year programs as well, I needed to use the new computerized ERAS system, whose motto is "We can lose your completed application faster than the U.S. Post Office." I got the computer disks, familiarized myself with the 284-page instruction booklet, typed in my information, including a new personal statement explaining how excited I would be to get a well-rounded preliminary year that included more than just internal medicine, and sent it off. This was interspersed with occasional phone calls to my research preceptor reminding him that he was now two weeks late in getting his letters of recommendation out and that if this continued I would be doing my residency at St. Horatio's Community Medical Building in Akron, Ohio.

Finally, I had everything neatly stacked in thirty-six piles and was nearly ready to send everything off, only two weeks late. I just needed to put labels on the envelopes, close them up, and mail them; this would be easy, I thought. Wrong! After spending eight hours trying to make mailing labels on the computer, I decided to do it by hand. Five grueling hours later, I held thirty-six sweat-streaked, blood-soaked manila envelopes, each filled with a different combination of papers saying exactly the same thing. After countless late nights and entire weekends devoted to assembling a bunch of applications whose success will be determined, basically, by my Board scores, I dropped them in the mail, never to see them again—except Yale's, which had the wrong mailing address.

Now I can sit back and relax with a rather senseless feeling of accomplishment. After all, I just *applied* to residencies—I didn't actually get one. But just by meeting UCSF's stringent application specifications, I felt as if I had taken great strides toward completing their dermatology residency, even though all I'd really done was tell them I'm interested in their program and that my Board scores were not as high as they would like.

Still, it feels as if I've overcome a great hurdle and there's nothing that can prevent me from getting the residency I want. I think it's important to have that sort of attitude as I head into the interviewing season, because that confidence, no matter how unfounded, becomes evident to everyone around me. So having given up most of my fall to put together these applications, I can now close my eyes and wait for the interview invitations to roll in.

But if I had to do it all over again, I would definitely get a secretary.

My Personal Statement
By Jeff Drayer

All my life, I've wanted to be a dermatologist. I first became aware of skin at a very early age. It seemed to me at the time that nearly everybody had some. Little did I know then how true that really was. And as I experienced various rashes during my youth, I realized that what I truly needed to do in life was cure disorders of the skin. But my interest in skin, much like a junctional nevus, really blossomed during adolescence, often aided by the use of various magazines. Looking back, I realize that all the psychiatrists were wrong—it was clearly my desire to perform shave biopsies that encouraged me to keep cutting my arms with razor blades. My zeal for dermatology has continued to grow and becomes firmer each day, not unlike an actinic keratosis.

But why dermatology? Many people believe it is because dermatologists have almost no call, don't work on weekends, don't deal with sick people, have patients who can actually pay, don't need to know much about medicine, and take long vacations. As evidenced by the fields I originally considered—radiology and ophthalmology—nothing could be farther from the truth. Then why? Perhaps it's my morbid obsession with warts that haunts me each night as I try to sleep. Perhaps it's my disgust for ugly people. Whatever the reason, I know that, like a blue nevus, this desire is something deep within me.

There are many things that make me perfect for the field of dermatology. The aforementioned interest in skin, I believe, makes me highly qualified for this demanding area of expertise. My ability to describe things as "erythematous" or "macular" certainly meets or exceeds that of my peers. In addition, I truly dislike dealing with sick people, or any of their fluids, and I feel that dermatology will give me the opportunity to care for patients who don't really have anything medically wrong with them. Also, I find I am more coherent and make fewer mistakes after eleven hours of sleep, which is why I have not pursued my true love, vascular surgery. And let's face it, having uncontrollably shaky hands is far less dangerous during a skin biopsy than during a femoral bypass. Moreover, at some point I'm going to have to swear something about doing no harm or whatever, and a field that involves merely choosing the right steroid cream for each patient affords me the least likelihood of getting sued.

In conclusion, I would like to say that I realize that dermatology is perhaps the hardest specialty to match in. Nevertheless, over the past four years, I have worked very hard in ways that may not come across well in things like "grades" or "letters of recommendation." I stand out in the intangibles, such as my ability to gain rapport with patients by first making fun of their skin disorder, but then slowly appearing to accept them, thus alleviating their fears. As can be seen by my extensive research into hard-to-detect pulmonary nodules, I have also learned both to appreciate the scientific method and to alter my data imperceptibly so as to make it coincide with my hypothesis, skills which I believe will serve me well in my many future research endeavors. I can also play the 'Star Spangled Banner' on the kazoo, with my nose.

I submit, then, my application to your esteemed program in dermatology. I sincerely look forward to the opportunity to work with you and your residents in your fine department, as well as to learning Spanish if you are one of the programs in the Caribbean to which I am applying. I happily anticipate an interview so I can get to know and appreciate your program: Just don't schedule me for the week of January 3–10, as I will be helping certain friends of mine carry some items very legally across the Mexico–Texas border.

The Virtual Physician

So, after several clinic-based rotations—dermatology, rheumatology, radiation oncology, and now ophthalmology—I've seen quite a few patients. I've listened to their questions, and tried to give them answers and assuage their fears. Of course, as a fourth-year student, I don't always have the answers. Which is why, each day when I come home from work, I think the same thing to myself: thank God for the Internet.

Now of course, the nerds in my former lab were sorely disappointed by how little time I spent searching the Web. As a matter of fact, I don't actually own a computer. But, as I've discovered, all my patients do. And they use it. Oh yes, they use it.

In the old days, sick people went to a doctor in search of professional advice—the kind that came from years of education and training. Little did I know how foolish those people were. Today, a patient can "know" all the "facts" about their medical condition after just a few clicks of the mouse. And many feel it is their responsibility to use this information to educate their doctors about that condition.

What could be better for a medical student than to be taught not only by residents and attendings but also by the patients themselves? How many times have I read a complicated chart, struggling to form the symptoms into a coherent pattern before entering a patient's room, only to be met by stacks of computer printouts with flashy titles such as "The Wild World of Psoriasis" and "Ginseng Cured My Ovarian Cancer!" Of course, no patient expects me to read all the material they have. So to save time, they conveniently highlight the "important" passages, such as how their arm pain and occasional stomachaches are classic symptoms of multiple sclerosis, and could they please have some plasmapheresis?

Yes, the Internet has been most helpful. How else could a patient know that we've incorrectly diagnosed his Budd-Chiari Syndrome as acne? In the past, patients were as helpless as seaweed, waving in the current of any whim their doctor devised. But now they are octupi and squid, empowered with thousands of suckers stuck to printouts full of knowledge. After all, if it's on the Internet it must be right and, besides, their cousin the chiropractor suggested a few sites on endometriosis. How could some doctor know more than the entire Information Highway? Moreover, people discover new cures for diseases every day—how could the busy King Med physicians possibly have time to keep current on them all?

Furthermore, there's information on the Net that the medical books don't discuss. Bogged down in "science" and "experiments," most textbooks have totally ignored the healing power of herbs. Fortunately, the Internet has not. Thanks to my helpful patients, I'm now well educated on the many uses of beeswax, which apparently cures bacterial infections and broken bones. Cabbage root salve not only clears up rosacea but also relieves migraines. Coriander is said to cure prostate cancer.

It's obvious that the Internet could be the solution to the country's health care problems. Fewer doctors' visits will be necessary since patients can solve most of their problems using search engines. Physicians' overhead costs will be significantly less, since their job will mostly be reduced to sitting at home answering the occasional phone call and fulfilling prescription requests from their Internet-educated patients.

So once again, I'd like to thank the Internet. Before it, patients were forced to listen to and respect doctors. They took their doctors' advice, swallowed bitter pills, and, insofar as medical science was able, were healed. But now, patients can attempt to treat themselves, no matter how poorly they understand their condition or how much insurance they have.

But perhaps the medical profession can also learn something from the Internet. After all, through the use of pretty colors and clever slogans, it has turned the patient population into an insane army of zealots. And why not? The Internet doesn't make them sit for three hours in a waiting room reading ancient *Car and Driver* magazines before they are told to undress and sit on cold tables just to have their plantar warts palpated for the thousandth time. It's open 24 hours a day, always listens, and can be programmed to flash updates of the day's football scores. Free from the icy grasp of insurance conglomerates, the Internet reaches into thousands of homes, costs almost nothing to use and, best of all, can be wrong as much as it wants and still not have to buy malpractice insurance. It is all things to all patients—Hippocrates' vision of the ideal virtual physician.

Yes, thank God for the Internet.

Happy Trails To You

Well, it's been a long two months on the interview trail. And though my travels and efforts will probably not get me an actual residency, I'm left with something perhaps even more valuable: Knowledge. Since all my money, and many of my worldly possessions, have gone to American Airlines and Howard Johnson's, I now offer you my Insider's Guide to Interviewing. I hope with it you will fare better than I, and perhaps choose, at some later date, to compensate me for my invaluable help.

First, get a Ph.D. One would think that a program with a clinical opening would not be interested in an applicant's fascinating eight-year hunt for Interleukin-18 and, actually, they're not. However, they do want to know that you're willing to withstand years and years of mindless torture with no obvious return on your miserable investment—these are the kind of people they want drawing their blood cultures at 4:00 A.M. If it's too late for you to get a Ph.D., hint that you might be willing to get one. By the time you're sitting in front of them with no earthly idea of how the unfolding of protease complexes can prevent virus migration, you've already got your interview and it's too late for them to withdraw their invitation.

Next, make sure that you have one very good question. Most interviewers don't know anything about you, haven't read your application materials, and don't much care what you've done in the past. They just know they have to spend fifteen minutes talking to you without looking like an idiot. The easiest way to do that is to introduce themselves and then cleverly ask if you have any questions about the program. Since you investigated the program before you came, had dinner with the residents the night before, attended the program coordinator's information session earlier that morning, listened to the chairman's half-hour speech, and took the seven-hour tour of the hospital, you already know everything—including the receptionist's agonizingly long story about how she came to be part of the program and knows more about it than any of the doctors. You probably even know where they keep the free drug samples. But you can't look "uninterested" and not ask a question, or you will spend several very awkward minutes with a guy who considers the highlight of his day to be freezing "a really big wart,"

So you need one good question that you'll ask each of your twenty-three interviewers. It doesn't really matter which question you use—my favorite was "Will my sexually transmitted diseases place your particular patient population in any additional danger?" Just make sure that when you ask it, your facial expression conveys deep concern. Then nod your head knowingly for the next ten minutes as they tell you how much they like the current residents, that they were offered several better jobs but came to this program because it has a "much better environment," that the crime rate in their city is overstated, and how well their son's soccer team is doing this season. Afterward, they'll shake your hand, thank you for coming, and, as you leave, lean back in their chair soaking in the warm glow of another successfully completed interview while jotting down how very interested and well-qualified you appeared to be.

The next thing you need to know about interviewing is how to get along with the residents. As opposed to your rotations, here you can't simply win their love by begging to do all their manual disimpactions while writing their talk on osteoporosis. In the interview setting, you have to make the residents like you based only upon who you are. Luckily, you can still fool them. But beware: they'll tell you they have nothing to do with where on the list you get ranked and therefore you can ask them your real questions, including "How late do residents stay at night?" and "Is there random drug testing?" This is not true. These people will have to work with you, and if they don't like you, they'll make certain you don't get in. Therefore, make sure you laugh at their stupid jokes, act amused by the story about how a resident almost killed someone by confusing the potassium syringe with the saline syringe, and never, ever, ask them any of your real questions. Remember, residents hate every-third-night call more than anything in the world and the number one quality they're looking for in a new resident is the willingness to do ten straight months in the MICU. Just make sure you associate yourself right away with the interviewee who spends all his time sucking up to the chief resident and taking notes on the notepad he has in his briefcase. If you do, you'll hear the answers to all your questions anyway.

If interviewers do actually ask you a question, remember that no one is interested in your research on ICAM-26 in salamander eggs, just the fact that you have a high threshold for being treated like pond scum. Don't forget, the pediatrician interviewing you doesn't want to hear about any of it, mostly because he's never heard of ICAM-26, and who the hell does this punk think he is, telling me that I'm a bad doctor because I don't cut up lizard eggs? No, they really want to hear a recapitulation of the chairman's speech. That way, you're in no danger of presenting new ideas which, as far as the faculty is concerned, can only lead to independent thinking. And it also lets them know how incredibly well you'll fit into the department. Because they don't care what your grades are, how many papers you've published, or how intricately you know the coagulation cascade—all they care about is that you're not going to make Trouble. They've got a busy daily schedule of earaches that they want you to see for them, and they don't want your mind so consumed with the vagaries of the sodium-hydrogen pump in fetal platypus hepatic cells that you can't see their patients and fill out their paperwork.

Once you've proven that you are a friendly, easygoing person who's willing to work whatever hours they want doing whatever they want you to do, it's time to go back to your hotel room and write thank-you letters. As you struggle through the eighth letter looking for a new way to say how impressed you were with the department's dedication to the surgical treatment of surgical problems through the use of surgery, you might wonder why you have to thank someone for interviewing you, a qualified applicant, for a job that he has to fill? This is a very good question. But never ask it again, since not writing a thank-you letter somehow translates into being the kind of resident who might not be willing to take the blame during a malpractice lawsuit. Make sure that you write a letter full of words interspersed with occasional punctuation. And end it with your name in big, bold letters, so that it will become imprinted on their retinas, allowing them to see it even in their dreams.

Here's another bit of advice before you hit the interview trail: make sure you have at least $700,000 in the bank. This is what it will cost when St. Bartholomew's Lady of the Blessed Scalpel Hospital calls and tells you to be in Manitoba by the next morning for an interview. So, since you will have to pay for your hotel and food (minus the $1.75 they give you to spend in the hospital's cafeteria), start selling your jewelry and family heirlooms now. This way you can avoid having to sell them for whatever price the guy outside the bus station is willing to pay, and you won't have to sleep on the urology floor again.

Finally, don't apply in dermatology. There are, apparently, only two spots in the entire country and, no matter how much you debase yourself, they don't want to interview you.

So there it is, my guide to successfully interviewing for residency positions. As you follow these simple guidelines, make sure you take in and critically evaluate everything you see as you travel from hospital to hospital. And if you happen to notice that any programs are in need of an extra dermatology resident, remember that my number at my parents' house will always be listed in the telephone book.

Thanks For The Memories

Dear Dr. Thrombus,

Hi—I just wanted to send you a quick note of thanks for interviewing me for your internal medicine internship position. I truly enjoyed meeting with your two faculty interviewers. I was particularly pleased to recite the basic points of my personal statement while they flipped through my application to familiarize themselves with my background.

The two hours of attending rounds that I was able to sit through were also very interesting. And while these were, in fact, exactly the same as the hundreds of other attending rounds I've sat through in the past, I nevertheless appreciated the chance to pay to fly to your city to hear one of your third-year medical students present a case of pneumonia.

I also felt I learned a lot by attending your residents' morning report. Although, as someone applying for an internship year, I'll never actually be invited to a resident's morning report, I nevertheless found yesterday's case of alcoholic cirrhosis fascinating. And, finally, the opportunity to sit in a room for an hour with the other forty students applying for this one spot was very nice. It's refreshing to meet young people and future colleagues so enthusiastic about your program that they traveled at their own expense just for the opportunity to briefly see your campus without even receiving lunch.

So once again, thank you very much for taking the time out of your busy schedule to speak with me, an applicant whom you believe qualified to occupy a job opening which you need to fill in order to continue to run your program. Thank you very much.

Sincerely,

Jeff Drayer

Road Warrior 2

Today I was driving down University Road in the pouring rain on my way home from the hospital. Suddenly, as if in slow motion, I watched as the car in front of me tried to make a left turn while another car barreled down the opposite lane at about 40 mph. The laws of physics being relatively stable, even in North Carolina, it goes without saying that the front of the oncoming car plowed into the side of the one that was turning, nestling snugly into its side much like a protein into an enzyme with a very high specificity. From what I can tell, there aren't that many car accidents in this town: It just seems that I'm there every time one happens.

Not wanting to get wet, my first thought was that I should just stay in the car. Since I have no idea how to treat someone who's been in a car accident unless they also happen to have rheumatoid arthritis or glaucoma, my second thought was that I should definitely stay in the car. My third thought was that I had probably contaminated myself anyway. Nevertheless, perhaps out of some primal fear that I'd get yelled at by an attending if I didn't, I decided to get out of my car and try to help.

I was the first one there, and I saw that the girl driving the turning car had a cut on her chin but was still conscious. I thought back to our basic life-saving course during my first year when, fortunately, I still had an attention span of five minutes, and recalled that the first thing to do was to tell someone to call 911. I ran to the nearest car and instructed the driver to do so. Unfortunately, I stopped paying attention to the BLS instructor shortly after learning that part, and I simply could not think of what else to do.

Several people had gathered around by now, but no one was making any doctor-like noises, so I closed my eyes and tried to think of any little bits of information about this sort of situation that my professors had tried so hard to teach me. I recalled something about not moving any necks or spines. That sounded pretty reasonable, I thought. But, it would make it awfully hard to get her out of the car, which had begun to generate some pretty funny smells.

So I thought of a compromise. "Can you move your neck and arms?" I asked. Maybe this was the right thing to ask and maybe it wasn't, but she was so hysterical it didn't matter. I may as well have asked if she thought it would be selling out to do liposuction and cosmetic laser surgery after enduring so many years of education and training. I looked at her pupils; they seemed pretty normal. As normal, at least, as those of any patient for whom I'd confidently written "PERLA" in an admission note.

"Can you see me clearly?" I asked. I noticed then, as she mumbled something about her driver's license being melted, that all the people around me were standing back, allowing me to be in charge. "Can you see me?!" I shouted. She looked up at me, a bit taken aback, and nodded her head. "Are you dizzy?!" She shook her head no. "Are you hurt?!" She paused and then pointed to her ankle. I quickly felt it for any protruding bones and, not seeing any blood on her pant leg, asked if she could walk.

As it turned out, she could not walk very well. I imagined a room full of lawyers and one young girl, wrapped from thigh to toe in bandages, all pointing their fingers at me as the judge assigned damages of one-third of my future earnings ($546) for permanently robbing this girl of the ability to walk. So I carried her over to the curb, while a middle-aged man in a double-breasted suit asked if he should get some blankets from his car. I said yes, and I gently set her down on the curb and covered her with them.

She was sobbing uncontrollably now, taking me back to my days in Clinical Arts when patient-actors would begin to cry at the slightest provocation, such as seeing the med student take a stethoscope out of his bag. But it also made me think that maybe I should actually talk to this girl, who was now clutching my arm and wailing into my chest. Obviously, "What brings you here today?" was out of the question. And my tragically limited experience in talking to girls made it all the more difficult. Finally, my four years of rigorous studying and my clinical training from some of the finest physicians in the world enabled me to lean over and do what probably every person there had been wanting me to do for some time—ask her name.

I sat there on the curb with her for about five more minutes until the ambulance arrived. Once she started talking, she calmed down and didn't even notice that I couldn't think of any good medical questions to ask her. The paramedics came over. I told them about her ankle and that she seemed fine neurologically, with normal pupils, good vision, no vomiting, and normal cognitive ability. They thanked me and I walked away.

Of course, she could very well have lacerated her spleen with a cracked rib (I think—I don't remember much anatomy these days) and be hemorrhaging internally. But she was on her way to the hospital and besides, there was nothing I could have done about it. In fact, I hadn't done much at all, other than sit and talk with her.

But as I walked away, several people came over and shook my hand and thanked me, much as they had in similar circumstances three years ago. One even went so far as to say that had I not taken charge, they wouldn't have known what to do. I couldn't recall actually taking charge, and I suddenly realized my legs were still a little shaky. However, as I drove home, it occurred to me that maybe the bystander had been right. This time I had indeed given the impression of, if not actually felt, confidence in my ability. And, as I've learned from just about every experience I've had in my two years on the wards, it doesn't matter whether or not you know what you're doing—all that matters is that people think you know.

In actuality I hadn't done so badly. Certainly, after four years of med school, I could have known a lot more about how to handle the situation. But everything worked out all right. And just as I was a little better this time than last, so I would be a bit better in the future. Medicine, they tell us, is a lifetime of learning. So maybe I really am on my way to becoming a doctor. Hopefully, the judge will appreciate that when, in the very near future, I get subpoenaed.

Match Day

Finally, The Day had come. During the last four years, I had diligently memorized old exams the night before tests, pretended to know how to draw blood before finally asking my resident to help me, and toiled at least fifteen hours a week typing numbers into the correct columns of my pulmonary nodule database. And all my hard work had boiled down to this one day: Match Day.

The phrase, of course, inspires hope in the minds of med students everywhere. It is the beacon of light at the end of a very, very dark tunnel, the pot of gold at the end of an interminably long rainbow, the clear margin beneath the Clark level-IV melanoma. It was what got us through countless boring genetics lectures and the long nights on call with annoying pediatric residents. For years, it had been in our thoughts, our conversations, and our dreams. And, finally, it had come.

I made my way nervously to Dolor Auditorium, fearful that all the free food had been eaten already. But even though it had not, the butterflies in my stomach would not let me eat any more than four plates of fried mozzarella sticks. Obviously, I was scared.

And why shouldn't I be? After all, somewhere at the front of the room lay an envelope that contained the secret to my future. After years and years of schooling, months of applying to programs, and weeks of interviewing—all for the low cost of $786,943.19—the course of my next four years, and beyond, had finally been determined.

I got in line and made my way slowly toward the pile of envelopes. "Aamer Farooki," I stated to the woman who asked me my name. She looked through the stack but found nothing; he had already picked his up. Damn, I thought, as I gave her my real name. I had been so close.

I clutched the envelope tightly and made my way to the back of the auditorium, the same auditorium where the deans had welcomed us almost four years ago. Around me, people were laughing, yelling, hugging, even kissing. I turned and looked at the envelope in my hands. With a deep breath, I closed my eyes and slowly tore it open, just as I'd done for four years in my dreams. Where would I go? What was my ultimate fate? This was the culmination of medical school, right there in front of me. I opened my eyes. And there, written in large capital letters, was the phrase

"BOSTON GENERAL-MA DERMATOLOGY S."

Oh.

It wasn't my first choice. It wasn't my last. In fact, it made me about the fourth happiest person I could be. Which was fine, I supposed. I looked around. There was no fanfare. No trumpets or gun volleys or musicals based on my life. Just me and an envelope: Boston General derm. Okay. Now what?

Then it occurred to me: the only thing left was to go ahead and start being a doctor. Did I really have to do that? I mean, the Match had always sort of been the ultimate goal. It was fun trying to guess where I would end up. I never really figured there was something afterwards. But, apparently, there was. This Match was telling me that I was going to have to go to Boston and actually become a dermatologist. That hadn't occurred to me until that very moment. A dermatologist, huh? Like, seeing acne and rashes all day? How about that.

I sat down on a table in the corner and took it all in. So, I was actually going to be something other than a medical student soon. It was hard to believe. Over the course of my education, I had learned to take things in small steps rather than looking at the whole scary picture. And, since the Match had always loomed as the Final Step, I had never looked past it. Well, now I had reached it, and there was nowhere to go but forward. It felt weird.

I sat and watched the moving picture in front of me: The people I had spent every single day of the last four years with, the people whom I had met as mere MS-Is, were all laughing and talking with each other, happy to have come to the end. And as I looked at these people I had grown so close to, and who were now on the verge of becoming doctors, I felt something welling up in my stomach. The feeling was all-encompassing, spreading out to my limbs, my head, and my heart. It was a feeling that I had experienced before, long ago, and now, watching my happy fellow students, it came back a hundred times more strongly. It was the realization that *I don't know anything about medicine.*

I had always pushed the feeling aside, always hoped it would go away. Eventually I'll be a fourth-year student, I'd tell myself. Eventually I'll match. By then, everything will be fine. But I had just been lying to myself. It had become obvious to any friend or family member who ever had to listen to me stumble my way incorrectly through the answer to a medically related question. It had been clear to every patient whom I, as a fourth-year medical student, had asked where exactly his anterior cruciate ligament was located. It had certainly been obvious to the residency directors; in fact many still use the parts of my application that are not streaked with my blood and sweat as scrap paper. And now it was obvious to me.

But as I watched the room begin to clear, the soon-to-be-doctors going off to celebrate their new futures, I was struck by a thought. What I had witnessed this Match Day was a scene that had played itself out in every medical school across the country. And most of those graduates would become good, competent residents. A few of them, in fact, would be going to the same program as I was. And they, just like my friends in med school, would be able to adequately cover up the fact that I didn't know, for example, the difference between the epidermis and the dermis. Maybe, it occurred to me, I could sneak through this stuff for another four years. I thought deeply about it for a moment. Yes, I decided, I bet I could. A thin smile spread across my face, and I went off to join in the celebration.

The Oath

So this is it. The end. After a very long initiation into the field of Medicine, it is now only a matter of days before I am placed in its ranks forever, an irreversible situation until someone discovers that I'm prescribing way too much morphine and that my lower back feels really, really good. Of course, my classmates and I must first participate in a symbolic rite of passage: the recital of the Hippocratic Oath. This renowned Oath is one of Western Civilization's oldest and greatest traditions, its repetition the only thing left separating physicians from physician's assistants. So, as the long-awaited day loomed closer, I decided to look at this Oath to see just what I was going to be saying. And what I found, to my surprise and disappointment, is that a lot of the Hippocratic Oath is wrong.

The first problem is that it was written in Ancient Greek, a language that has been extinct for over 2000 years. But even the English translation is troublesome. So, as a service to all the med students who someday will stand before the eyes of Apollo the physician, I will point out a few of the problems so that each of you can decide whether this particular Oath is the one you want to take.

"I will reckon him who taught me this Art equally dear to me as my parents." Now, I love my parents, who always told me things like "just try your best" and "even if you don't know how to take a blood gas, we still love you." I could never have gotten through med school without their support. But then I think of some of the conversations I had on surgery, such as:

Attending: "What artery is that?"

Drayer: "The superior mesenteric?"

Attending: [silence]

Drayer: "The femoral?"

Attending: "Stop retracting like a girl."

And I wonder if reckoning them as my parents would, in the long run, necessarily be the best thing for me.

"By precept, lecture, and every other mode of instruction, I will impart a knowledge of the Art to my own sons and those of my teachers, and to disciples bound by a stipulation and oath according to the law of medicine, but to none others." First of all, my sons will never become doctors. From the day when everyone's father visits the second grade classroom to talk about what they do, my sons will know the shame of having a dad who needed eight years of specialized training to prescribe the same steroid cream for every rash known to man. And when they later find out, as I have, that girls just don't find guys who are good at science and owe $87,904 terribly attractive, that will clinch the deal.

As to imparting my knowledge only to those bound by oath according to the laws of medicine, I'm sure that eventually I will be expected to teach registered nurse dermatologists and other well-qualified high school graduates how to do my job so they can run me out of business. This is the kind of moral quandary I have, so far, successfully escaped for most of my life. But, since my every future action, including what I eat for dinner and how much television I watch, will be dictated by my HMO, there may be no escaping this one. Luckily, by that time, most of my synapses used to store medical knowledge will once again be filled with baseball statistics.

"I will follow that system of regimen which, according to my ability and judgment, I consider for the benefit of my patients." This, of course, is simply not cost-effective. Imagine what would happen if we treated people the way we thought was best for them. Soon people would be getting all sorts of subspecialty consults, expensive medications, and high-tech treatments, the sort of things that would put managed care operations right out of business! If the patients became the number one concern, I would never be able to collect my monetary incentives for not spending money on their treatment. Hippocrates obviously could not envision how ludicrous his ideas would be in the unavoidable future of health care as controlled by businessmen and the spouses of elected officials.

"I will abstain from whatever is deleterious and mischievous." If taken seriously, this would put a complete end to gynecological surgery.

"I will give no deadly medicine to anyone if asked." This is a tough one. Can I really prevent my patients from deciding to take their steroid creams orally? Besides, do I know how the tetracycline is going to react with the several pounds of ginseng, beeswax, and shark cartilage they've ingested that day? I believe this sentence should be replaced with, "I will prescribe to my patients only water."

"With purity and with holiness I will pass my life and practice my Art." A study is now underway to show that practicing one's Art in holiness is no longer cost-effective. After all, purity is expensive and very time consuming. Perhaps "efficiency and shrewdness" would be more appropriate.

"I will not cut persons laboring under the stone, but will leave this to be done by men who are practitioners of this work." I don't think anyone really knows what this means, though I'm sure it somehow now falls under the auspices of an "allied health professional."

"Into whatever houses I enter, I will go into them for the benefit of the sick." What a pain in the neck this would be! Every party I ever attend has to be for the benefit of the sick? Every time I get invited somewhere for dinner it's for the benefit of the sick? Whenever I pick up my kids from their friends' houses? If my car breaks down and I need to use a phone? Can I bill for those hours?

"I will abstain from the seduction of females or males." Had I known about this female thing, I never would have gone to medical school in the first place.

"While I continue to keep this Oath unviolated, may it be granted to me to enjoy life and the practice of the Art, respected by all men, in all times. But should I trespass and violate this Oath, may the reverse be my lot." Well, what are the odds of this really happening? Will the reverse be my lot if I enter one house not to the benefit of the sick? Am I constantly going to be looking over my shoulder, wondering if I just failed to abstain from something mischievous, if I just made that one mistake and am now disrespected by all men at all times? How could I enjoy a life like that? Even murderers get three strikes. No, I don't like this lot-reversing part one bit.

So, it's obvious that doctors in the Twenty-First Century should have second thoughts about taking an Oath as antiquated as this. Therefore, I would like to introduce a new oath, one which may soon be used by most of the progressive medical schools across the country and which will make Hippocrates as distant a memory as Galen, Maimonides, and Klaxos the Trephiner.

The Drayocratic Oath

I swear by Sandoza the Insurer and all its actuaries and accountants that, according to my ability and amount of free time, I will keep this Oath. I will practice my Art as best I can on those who can pay for my services or who ask me nicely, but never on those who demand it as if my work were their right. I will carefully explain to my patients that I'm trying to help them and that, no matter what they read on the Internet, antibiotics sometimes work even better than bloodwort and are just as "natural." I will, if necessary, refresh the minds of physicians' assistants as to the meaning of the word "assistant." I will continue to have a life outside the hospital, remembering that I am a person too and don't have to give in to every one of my patients' demands, no matter how ridiculous they are. I will never refer to my colleagues as "health care providers." I will remember that I went into this profession because it is something I enjoy, and not because childhood issues have forced me to become obsessed with taking care of people who nevertheless don't trust me. I will, to the best of my ability, treat those who want to get better, but will send those who insist upon wasting my time to a psychologist or, perhaps, an optometrist. I will not prescribe only drugs made by companies who fly me out to "conferences" on tropical islands, but let it be known that such flying cannot realistically be totally divorced from my drug-prescribing decisions. While I continue to keep this Oath unviolated, may it be granted to me to enjoy life, the practice of the Art, and the three hot tubs placed strategically throughout my house. But should I violate this Oath, allow me to enjoy only one hot tub.

Galen

Galen of Pergamum (A.D. 130-201), the Greek physician whose writings guided medicine for more than a millenium after his death, inspired the name, Galen Press. As the father of modern anatomy and physiology, Galen wrote more than one hundred treatises while attempting to change medicine from an art form into a science. As a practicing physician, Galen first ministered to gladiators and then to Roman Emperor Marcus Aurelius. Far more than Hippocrates, Galen's work influenced Westen physicians and was the "truth" until the late Middle Ages when physicians and scientists challenged his teachings. Galen Press, publishing non-clinical, health-related books, will follow Galen's advice that "the chief merit of language is clearness . . . nothing detracts so much from this as unfamiliar terms."

About the Author

Jeffrey A. Drayer, M.D. is currently a transitional intern in San Diego, Calif. He began writing at the age of 14, and started placing words together into complete sentences at 21. He attended Cornell University, earning his degree in Psychology in 1993. Despite the events outlined in this book, he then received his M.D. degree from Duke University in 1998. Dr. Drayer plans to enter his dermatology residency in Boston, Mass., in 1999, and the Baseball Hall of Fame in 2017.

The Cost-Effective Use of Leeches and Other Musings of a Medical School Survivor

Also by Galen Press. Ltd.:

After-Death Planning Guide
  by Kenneth V. Iserson, M.D.

Death Investigations: The Basics
  by Brad Randall, M.D.

Death To Dust: What Happens To Dead Bodies?
  by Kenneth V. Iserson, M.D.

Ethics in Emergency Medicine, 2nd ed.
  Edited by Kenneth V. Iserson, M.D. Arthur B. Sanders, M.D.,
  and Deborah Mathieu, Ph.D.

Get Into Medical School! A Guide for the Perplexed
  by Kenneth V. Iserson, M.D.

Getting Into A Residency: A Guide for Medical Students, 4th ed
  by Kenneth V. Iserson, M.D.

Getting Into A Residency Companion Disks
  DOS and Windows™ versions

House Calls, Rounds, and Healings: A Poetry Casebook
  by David Schiedermayer, M.D.

Non-Standard Medical Electives in the U.S. & Canada, 1998-1999
  by Kenneth V. Iserson, M.D.

The International Medical Graduate's Guide to U.S. Medicine, 2nd ed.
  by Gloria A. Goldman, J.D.

Resumes And Personal Statements for Health Professionals, 2nd ed.
  by James W. Tysinger, Ph.D.

For more information, please contact:

Customer Service
Galen Press, Ltd.
P.O. Box 64400
Tucson, AZ 85728-4400   USA
Internet: Http://www.galenpress.com
Tel: (520) 577-8363   Fax: (520) 529-6459